Mark Twain on the Mississippi

Earl Schenck Miers

MARK TWAIN ON

THE MISSISSIPPI

Illustrated by ROBERT FRANKENBERG

THE WORLD PUBLISHING COMPANY
Cleveland and New York

c.3

Library of Congress Catalog Card Number: 57:5892

This book is dedicated to

WILLIAM TARG

who first suggested that I write it

Contents

CONTENTS

Author's Note

In hannibal, missouri, in the 1840's there lived a boy named Sam Clemens. Townspeople often shook their heads and wondered to what sad end this lad would come, for when a boy is in part Tom Sawyer and in part Huckleberry Finn he possesses a better than average capacity for mischief. This story is about Sam and how he grew up to become Mark Twain, one of our most beloved Americans. Sam's story is presented as fiction, but it is largely truth, and the *Postscript* explains where fact and fancy divide.

E.S.M.

Mark Twain on the Mississippi

1.

Sam Clemens, Sinner

About an hour before dawn, on a spring morning in 1843, the town of Hannibal, Missouri, fought a duel with the devil. Young Sam Clemens awoke, sitting straight up in bed while a clammy chill ran along his spine.

Nowhere did thunder ever sound so loud as it did in the river country. Give any clap of thunder a good start down the Mississippi, and it rolled up to a town like a steamboat with her boilers hissing, striking the place with a bang that shook houses and lifted branches from trees and maybe even knocked down tombstones in the graveyard.

"That was a whammer," Sam muttered, shivering at the echoes that rolled ominously across Holliday's Hill. He tried to scratch the itch from beneath his sandy hair, but the prickles of fear wouldn't go away.

All at once, as Sam's heart thumped, the town seemed to glow with an ugly flash, and two prongs of purplish fire reached across the sky.

"That's Satan all right—that's the devil waving his arms," breathed Sam, for he considered himself an authority on how the keeper of the lower regions worked while the rest of the world slept. "He's a-reaching out to grab some sinner."

Again, far down the Mississippi, rumbling thunder began

to gather strength for another whack at the town. Sam gulped, recognizing what this new threat might mean. With the next clap, Satan's arms would reach out once more, and maybe this time—

"Oh, Lord!" Sam groaned, and slid under the sheet, and then pulled the pillow over his head, hoping that might help too.

For Sam knew. *He* could be the sinner that Satan wanted to catch. Even at the age of almost eight nobody became an authority on wickedness unless he worked at it. And there had to be a reason why Sam was awake while his younger brother Henry slept soundly. Henry was Ma's pet, the nearest Hannibal came to having an angel, which in Sam's opinion was as sickeningly close as any town should come.

Long before the second thunderclap rushed at Hannibal as though it wanted to hurl the town down the river to St. Louis, or maybe blow it clean out of the State of Missouri, Sam confessed a good many of his failings.

He, Sam Clemens, told lies, and often he told real whoppers, like the time he said he had attended Sunday school and instead had spent the morning swimming in Bear Creek with Will Bowen.

And he, Sam Clemens, never asked whose skiff he was taking when he wanted to sail over to Turkey Island, but borrowed any old skiff that was handy, hoping he could sneak it back without being caught.

And he, Sam Clemens, kept "bad company"—most of all, the company of that ragged river rat, Tom Blankenship, who everyone knew would die on the gallows unless somebody was thoughtful enough to shoot him first—and he, Sam Clemens, didn't care whom he teased, including his poor mother, by saying "Ma, I left something in my pocket for you," and then squealing with delight when she pulled out the dead bat.

Sam shivered afresh, nowhere near the bottom of the list of his wickedness when, from beneath sheet and pillow, he heard the second crackling snap of thunder and glimpsed the fiery edges of light filling the room. For a fearful moment he waited, breathing hard, and then he murmured with a wonderful sense of escape, "I did it again. I slipped straight through his fingers!"

Sam's head popped from beneath the pillow. He wasn't entirely safe yet. He guessed he knew the rules of the devil's enterprises. Satan was entitled to three grabs before the contest ended, unless it began to rain. What the rain had to do with calling quits to this grisly game of tag, even Tom Blankenship didn't know. "Why is vinegar good for warts?" was all Tom could say, as though that was any answer. Still, Sam was willing to believe in salvation from any quarter, and as he waited, head still raised but ready to duck for the pillow at the first sound of danger, new grumbles seemed to be gathering in the old river's throat. With added heart Sam muttered vows of eternal virtue. He would never lie, cheat, skip school, steal a skiff. He would obey his parents, and grownups would say no boy ever possessed better manners. He—he—

Sweetly, gently, the rain splattered on the roof and against the window and upon the limbs of trees bursting with the leaves of a bright, warm spring. Sam sighed, closed his eyes, and fell into a blissful sleep.

Sunlight filled the room when Sam reawakened. He could hear birds singing, a dog barking, the rattle of a wagon lumbering down the hill toward the river. Henry, an early riser, was already downstairs.

Sam gazed at the streaks of light on wall and ceiling, wriggled his toes, and recalled the dark musings that had disturbed him during the storm. Somehow with daylight Sam lost interest in salvation. Soon only one thought absorbed him, a wish that he possessed the talent of Gull Brady. Gull could snap his big toe so that the sound could be heard thirty feet away. Sometimes Gull could make his pet dog come running just by snapping his big toe.

Sam cocked his head toward the window, and presently a muffled meow sounded in the yard. Sam hopped from the bed and leaned out the window.

"You told me to call," Tom Blankenship hissed.

"Wait there," Sam hissed back, then ducked his head from view.

"I thought you must have broke a leg," Tom said critically when in no more than ten winks Sam popped through the window and slid to the ground.

"My Ma will bust my hide if we don't get out of here quick," Sam grumbled.

"Then let's *git*," Tom agreed, and his long legs led the race down Hill Street toward the river. For the first time, Sam noticed the bulge of Tom's pockets, and when they could stop, Tom took out four potatoes.

"I got them down to Selmes's store."

"They're sure whoppers," Sam remarked admiringly. He didn't ask whether Mr. Selmes had been a willing party to this transaction. Sam knew how Tom had acquired those potatoes, considering he was always short of cash.

"We'll roast 'em for breakfast," Tom decided. "We'll go over by Lover's Leap. The river's pretty there."

Sam nodded, breathing deeply and happily. There wasn't any better smell than the fragrance of locust trees in spring. There wasn't any better feeling than knowing a whole day of freedom and adventure stretched ahead.

In another hour Hannibal would shake off its drowsiness. Saturday always brought the hog drovers to town, and once they had delivered their swine at the pork houses near the mouth of Bear Creek, they were a lighthearted, money-spending crowd. They jammed Market Square, and kicked up the dust along the river front, and managed a couple of fist fights down at Wildcat Corner. Sam reckoned there wasn't any town that out-bustled Hannibal on a Saturday. The grand old Mississippi, rolling its mile-wide tide right up to Hannibal, made it the most important river port in Northern Missouri. Folks over in St. Joseph swore they lived at the gateway to the Great West, but Sam thought, Shucks, here's where the cargoes change boats for St. Jo. That place wouldn't be a hill of beans except for Hannibal.

Later, camped along the river at Lover's Leap, Sam watched the potatoes roasting a nice, crisp black. Tom broke open one of the skins, and the steam curled upward. Then, munching, he asked, "Sam, you hear the devil coming up the river early this morning?"

"I reckon I did."

"He scare you?"

"I guess not!"

"Me neither. Anyhow, it's Injun Joe he'd like to catch more'n us!"

Sam didn't answer at once. Somehow he had never been as afraid of Injun Joe as Tom. Shortcomings sometimes seemed to cling to Sam as fleas to a hound pup, but lack of sympathy for an underdog wasn't one. In all Hannibal, Sam couldn't think of anyone who lived a lonelier existence than Injun Joe. Fate had been against that poor Osage, even back in the days when he was a naked kid growing up in Oklahoma. One day the Pawnees caught Injun Joe, scalped him, and left the boy for dead. Luckily some cattlemen had stumbled on Injun Joe soon afterward, smacked him on the rump, and brought him back to life.

Sam had seen Injun Joe many times, hanging around the dock and hoping to pick up a little money fetching carpet-bags to the taverns for travelers on the steamers. A red wig covered the terrible scar on his head. And Sam had seen the large hollow sycamore up on Bear Creek where Injun Joe lived and did his cooking—not that he ever had much to cook.

"If you asked me," Sam said, "you leave Injun Joe alone, and he won't hurt you."

Tom hadn't asked Sam.

"A fellow who was meant to be dead and is still roaming the earth ain't up to no good. Especially an Injun." Tom could say the word "Injun" with a dark and evil sound, as though he expected any day Injun Joe would try to scalp everyone living in Hannibal. "That's how I see it," Tom declared, clearly surprised that the deed hadn't happened before now. "The Pawnees would have finished Injun Joe 'cept that there is more devil than human in Osages. You can't tell, Sam. Maybe Satan came up the river this morning to tell Injun Joe to sober up and get to scalpin', or he'd fix him good!"

Just then a noise sounded among the trees. Sam and Tom jumped as though, at that instant, an arrow had grazed both their britches. A fearful war whoop followed—luckily, in a high, squeaky voice that they both recognized.

"Hogtie you, Will Bowen!" Tom growled, swallowing his fright in a gulp of anger.

A boy about the age of Sam and Tom stepped forward. His face was so square that nature seemed to have hung a picture frame around his homeliness. Where Sam's hair was sandy, Will's was reddish, and where Tom had freckles on his nose and ears, Will's freckles splotched his entire face and made one think that somebody had taken a quill pen and splashed him with ink.

Tom grumbled, "People who sneak up and listen to private talk get their ears cut off."

"Sam's the one who's going to get cut up," Will announced. "No sooner than he gets home. I met Orion in

Market Square, and he says his Ma is laying for Sam for sneaking off."

"Orion can't handle Ma the way I can."

"You talk big."

"I know Ma. She's so softhearted she gets mad when a cat catches a mouse."

"Then your Pa'll lace you."

"Ma won't let him."

Tom flipped his head in an approving nod. Sam had the right idea, he maintained. Nobody could have a lick of fun without knowing how far they could go with grownups. Weak points had to be studied. Life would be nothing but work, school, and churchgoing otherwise. A boy would be worse off than a slave and where there were Fugitive Slave Laws now, mighty soon they'd be passing Fugitive Boy Laws. Yes, sirree, Tom said, parents didn't know how lucky they were, having boys who could get around them, and saving them the money to advertise for runaway boys who couldn't stand the drudgery any longer.

The magnificence of Tom's logic impressed Sam and Will. Even Gull Brady, who joined the gang toward the end of Tom's spiel, listened respectfully.

Sam broke the spell. The morning was melting clear away. If they didn't watch out, the morning steamer would come and go! "I'll race you," Sam shouted, off in a scamper.

Behind him trailed Tom, Will, and Gull. At Wildcat Corner a dozen more boys joined the chase. How dangerously long they had loitered was enough to chill the heart, for old John Hannicks, the Negro drayman who always managed to see the first smudge of smoke beyond the point, already had cackled his shrill summons: "Steeammm-*boat* a-comin'!"

Old Hannicks slapped his leg with glee. He knew how that cry could wake up Hannibal.

Sam's heart pounded with the thrill of the moment. There wasn't a loafer in Hannibal who wasn't stirring now. Nor a boy. There was just one grand tumble of long legs and short legs down the street to the river.

A sow and a litter of pigs rooting along the sidewalk scattered with frenzied squeals. Old "General" Gaines, napping in the shadow of a pile of skids, shook himself and sat up. Drays and carts clambered behind the men and boys.

Sam's eyes strained, taking in every detail of the two-chimneyed vessel spewing out smoke and sparks and gliding down the river with the haughty splendor of a king of the old Mississippi.

Long before the boat reached the dock two deck hands stood ready with the gangplank. A third swung a coil of rope, gauging his distance, an artist who could send that line

spinning across the water as unerringly as any cowhand ever roped a longhorn. The boat loomed closer and bigger. Out through the gauge cocks screamed the pent-up steam. The pilot lifted his hand. A bell rang. The wheels stopped, a bell clanged again, the wheels turned backward. The churning water spilled out a milky-white foam. The furnace doors, flung open, showed the pitch pine blazing and crackling.

Sam gazed at the gilded paddle boxes and read the boat's name—*Jeanie Deans*. She was a stunner!

"There's only two things in life I ever want to be," Sam sighed. "First would be a pirate."

"You ain't never going to be that," Tom answered. "Not a puny kid like you. Shucks, only one person in ten thousand can make a good pirate—or a fair-to-middlin' one, I reckon."

Sam didn't like being called puny. Any other time he'd

put a chip on his shoulder and dare Tom to knock it off for saying that. But the boat's whistle tooted again, the gangplank slammed into place, and Sam's glance returned to the pilot's cabin.

"That's the other thing I'd give most to be—a Mississippi River pilot!"

Will Bowen guffawed. Sam sounded like the biggest fool between Hannibal and St. Louis, which was stretching foolishness a long way.

"Only one in twenty thousand's born to be that," Will declared.

"Then I'm that one," Sam snapped back, working himself into a mood to fight both Tom and Will. But in the quarter where it counted most—where, soon enough, a real fight was coming—Sam had dropped his guard and knew it the moment a hand grasped his arm and a voice hissed over his shoulder:

"Ma knew all right where I'd find you!"

Sam turned to face Orion, his older brother.

2.

Sam and Henry

WILL, TOM, AND GULL rallied to Sam's defense.
"Why did you have to find him?"

"You let Sam go!"

"Any fathead can spoil a day's fun!"

Sam, too, joined the assault on Orion with fierce exuberance. "I thought you went to St. Louis to learn how to be a printer—not a snoop and a snitcher," he accused him.

Orion, awkward, humorless, and self-conscious of the beard he was trying to grow, answered stoically, "I went to St. Louis because Pa made me. And I found Sam because Ma asked me to."

Gull snapped his big toe and glared ferociously at Orion. Tom struck a pose of majestic defiance, hand thrust inside his ragged shirt so that he resembled Napoleon about to utter commands which would turn whole armies loose to conquer and slaughter the likes of Orion. Will Bowen glowered as his slow mind sorted out words of appropriate abuse, but Sam spoke first. "Aw, let's go home and get it over with," he said blithely. Orion smiled in a rather hang-doggish manner, which was what he had been doing for as long as Sam could remember.

Sometimes Sam couldn't decide whether it was Orion or

Injun Joe who deserved the distinction of being Hannibal's most luckless citizen. Nothing ever worked out right for Orion. When he tried to grow a little patch of vegetables, the sun beat down day after day until the vines withered into powdery limpness. If Orion planned a trip, rain fell in torrents. When Pa had opened a general store in Hannibal and made Orion his head clerk, affairs were in such a hopeless hodgepodge within a few weeks that only the field mice remained as steady customers. And Orion, wanting to be a lawyer ever since he could express an opinion in the matter, now found himself shunted off to St. Louis to become a printer. "Pa doesn't think I'm fit for anything but a mechanic," Orion had grumbled, revealing how deeply his pride had been wounded.

Understanding Orion made Sam sorry for him. There never was any sense trying to say anything bright to Orion. He wouldn't get the point. His mind always was somewhere else—off on a cloud or stuck in the mud like a Mississippi catfish.

They had reached Wildcat Corner before Orion broke the silence between them. "Shucks, Sam, I didn't want to be mean," he apologized. "I couldn't stand seeing Ma upset, and I knew you'd get around her somehow. I never could. I was the first-born, and I reckon they kind of practiced on me to see how hard they could knock a lad around without breaking his neck. But you can get away with murder."

Sam couldn't believe his ears. Orion had said something that was almost funny; it was a real belly-tickler for Orion. Sam grinned expansively, appreciating the miracle, and said, "I guess things must be going a little better in St. Louis."

Orion shrugged. "It could be worse, Sam. Since I read Benjamin Franklin's *Autobiography* and realized that he had to start life as a printer, it hasn't seemed so bad. You know, Franklin was quite a fellow. He's given me the right idea. If you eat nothing but vegetables and take cold baths and clear your mind in the morning by starting off with no more than a little bread and water, you'll soon feel fit as a fiddle."

A screechy fiddle, Sam thought cynically. But what could sound more like Orion, never satisfied with himself and wanting to be like someone else? Then, climbing Hill Street to the small house of white clapboards where the Clemenses lived, Sam's mind returned to more immediate concerns.

"You let me go in first," he told Orion.

"I don't see why."

"You don't have to see. A fugitive slave who is dragged home by the bloodhounds gets beat harder than one who shows up by himself, explaining that his absence was all a mistake!"

"Sam, Ma sent me . . ."

"Orion, you do as I say, or I'm not going in at all. You don't have to say that you caught me. Ma knows I couldn't miss seeing the *Jeanie Deans* dock. Confound it, you just better let me work this out my own way, or I'll tell Ma—I'll tell her—"

"What?"

"I don't know, but I'll think of something. And it'll be plenty awful!"

Orion's mouth tightened. "Oh, all right," he said. "I hate to think how hard it'll be for a liar like you to get into heaven."

"I've got to meet Ma before I meet St. Peter," Sam said, with a logic that even Orion could not dispute.

Sam went around to the back of the house, opened the kitchen door a crack, and peered in. At first, all he could see were cats—nineteen at the last count—for this was the spring when his mother had been unable to bear the thought of drowning one kitten.

A single glance revealed how much alike were Jane Clemens and her son Sam. His hair and hers were the same color. Chin and mouth looked alike, too, although Sam's eyes were a trifle bluer. The Southern drawl that marked Sam's speech came from her—"Sammy's long talk," she called it—and also his impulsiveness, the sense of disorderliness that drove both Orion and his father to the verge of distraction, and the quick wit with which neither could contend.

The woman knew the boy was there, although only his nose showed through the crack of the door's opening. "Come on in, Sammy," she said. "I can smell you even over these cats."

Sam entered the kitchen, shuffling his feet and hanging his head in a pose of abject remorsefulness.

"You going to lick me, Ma?"

"Sometimes it seems like an awful amount of effort for the little good it does. Where's Orion?"

"I don't rightly know."

"Well, I do. He's standing outside because you made him wait while you came in and hoodwinked me. You've tried that before, Sammy. Really, you must think I'm a very stupid woman."

"You're not, Ma."

"What'll you say after I horsewhip you?"

"We don't have a horsewhip."

"Then I can borrow one from old Mr. Blankenship."

"I didn't know you ever spoke to him, Ma."

Jane Clemens turned her head quickly and struggled not to smile. "I say hello to everybody," she said primly. "I always thought that there was a bit of good in everybody till I met you."

Sam edged over to the chair by the stove and sat down. Into his voice he forced his most pitiful tone. "Don't you love me, Ma?"

"I find it hard to say on Saturdays."

"What are you going to do with me, Ma?"

"Considering how little money we have, maybe I'll cut you up into a stew."

Orion blustered through the front door. "Did Sam come home?" he asked, red-faced with the shame of his deceit.

"He came home with you," the woman answered tartly. "You're easily led, Orion. I don't see that you're any better at telling a fib than Sammy, for all that you've had a ten-year start. If I had the strength, I'd lick you both, and I'd ask your father to do it if I didn't know he'd forget what I wanted before he got around to it. Some day when I'm dead you'll all be sorry."

Orion stood in the kitchen doorway, twisting his foot and looking sorry for himself. Sam took the practical view: "You'll look awfully pretty as an angel, Ma."

"You oughtn't to talk that way," Orion said soberly.

"No, you shouldn't," Jane Clemens admitted, thinking what a good disciplinarian Orion would make. "You're not going to get off scot-free, sneaking off like that, Sam. Causing me all that worry and Orion all the trouble of finding you. Just give me time, young Mr. Samuel Langhorne Clemens, and I'll think of something."

"Yes, Ma," Sam said, barely able to hide his grin. His mother, he reckoned, sounded severe only to impress Orion.

Footsteps outside the kitchen door announced the arrival of still another member of the Clemens clan. Henry Clemens, three years younger than Sam, was already a bookish, blue-eyed lad with curls that hung to his shoulders. Sam plastered his own hair with any kind of grease that would keep it flat. He accepted Henry as a brother because his mother said he must.

"Sam was down at the dock," singsonged Henry, wiping

his shoes before he entered the kitchen. "Sam was there when Orion catched him!"

Sam glowered, wondering whether to beat his younger brother with his fists or bounce a cobblestone off his fat, tattletale head. "Yes, I know," Mrs. Clemens said mildly. "Henry, your face is dirty."

"I'll wash it, Ma," Henry promised.

Sam looked away, disgusted at this rotten little do-gooder. Ten times a day Sam heard what a fine thing it would be if he were only more like Henry, and ten times a day Sam retorted, "Ma, why do you make me sick with such thoughts?"

And what did Orion say in such moments? "Now, Sam," pompous Orion pronounced, sounding like an owl who had learned to talk, "brothers should love one another!" What

Sam couldn't understand was why Pa had made a printer out of Orion. Why waste a born preacher?

Behind Henry appeared Sam's sister Pamela, eight years older than he, a shy, serious-minded girl with gray eyes and curly auburn hair. If Pamela was almost as humorless as Orion, Sam still felt that he should not tease her because of her delicate health and sweet, gentle disposition.

"Oh, Sammy's home," she said. "How nice!"

Jane Clemens sniffed. "Yes, Sam's home, and he can go straight to his room and stay there till I decide how to punish him."

"Don't be harsh on Sammy, Ma," Pamela pleaded.

Mrs. Clemens exhaled with exasperation. "This family—honestly, it will drive me mad! Orion would have me talk myself blue explaining to Sammy why he should be good, and Henry would like to see me nail his thumbs to the wall, and every time Sammy gets into mischief his sister thinks I should bake him a blackberry tart!" The woman's glance settled on Sam, who was enjoying immensely his position as the center of attention. "I thought I told you to go to your room," Jane Clemens exploded in sudden storminess. "Now you git."

Sam "got."

Almost two hours later a knock sounded on the door and Pamela entered, bringing Sam his lunch.

"How long is Ma going to keep me here?"

"A while yet."

"I could sneak out again!"

"Then Ma might station Henry by the window, or even here in the room, to watch you," Pamela suggested.

Sam blanched at the thought.

"She might even send Orion to give you a lecture."

"Stop!" Sam begged. "You've no right to torture me like this!"

Pamela looked genuinely contrite. "I have a message for you. From Tom Blankenship."

"Well, tell it!"

"I don't know whether I should," Pamela said honestly. "In a way it seems like getting around Ma."

"Oh, bother! What did Tom say?"

"That he'd give you 'the call' after supper. Also it would help if you could bring four or five cats."

Sam's puzzled frown was the forewarning of an approaching storm of questions. Already guilt-stricken that she had relayed even this much of the message, Pamela added hastily, "Now that's all I know, Sammy." But at the door she turned and said, "Except that Tom emphasized it would be better if they were large cats." Blushing furiously at her own implication in whatever treachery might be afoot, Pamela fled from the room.

Tantalized by the mystery that had been brought him, Sam scarcely touched his food. That Tom was a wizard for having ideas. Whatever scheme Tom had worked out involving cats should be a stunner, for Sam could sense the right ingredients for deviltry. Good old Tom never did things half way! "Who ever heard of a varmint being half-hung?" Tom always asked. In his opinion crimes should be conceived to fit the worst possible punishment.

But now Sam had a problem. When Tom said that he would call "after supper" he had meant "after dark"—Sam chuckled maliciously to think that Pamela had not guessed this coded significance in the message she had delivered. Sam would have to feign sleep in order to fool Henry, who always went to bed early, and then he'd have to sneak out—and back—without waking him. Sam had managed that feat before. The risks were relative; it was worse getting caught leaving than returning. Should Henry awaken, Sam knew that threats, or even a beating, wouldn't intimidate him as

long as Ma was within screaming distance. Somehow he'd
have to get out the window without waking Henry.

What staggered Sam, however, was the way those cats
complicated his problem. How would he get them through
the window without rousing Henry? Or how could he col-
lect half a dozen cats in the room and keep them there without Henry's knowledge?

Sam finally ate his lunch while he mused over this stumper.
When Pamela returned for his empty dishes, he queried her
sharply.

"Did Tom say to bring live cats?"

Pamela, almost as tenderhearted as her mother, retorted
uneasily, "Sammy, you and Tom wouldn't do anything to
hurt those cats?"

"Of course not," Sam lied gallantly. "That's why I was
sure Tom must have said to bring live cats. Oh, bother! You
can see the fix I'm in. How can I keep Henry from blabbing
and spoiling all the fun? Pamela, you've got to help me."

"I will not."

"You helped get me into this mess."

"Don't be ridiculous!"

Sam switched to a new tack, blinking his eyes as hard as
he could and managing to produce one or two tears. "Everybody's against me."

"Sammy, you know that isn't so."

"Ma's against me, and Henry and Orion, and now even
you!"

Pamela squirmed, knowing that by one ruse or another he
would ultimately trap her. "Sammy, what can I do?"

"You could hide four or five cats—big ones—in that old
unused chicken house."

"Suppose Ma found out?"

"You could blame it on Henry."

"Why, Sammy, I'd do no such thing!"

"Then blame it on me," Sam said. "Pa hates those cats. He'd be in a better mood if there were fewer of them around when he came home for supper. Everybody'd be happier!"

Pamela couldn't deny the soundness of this argument. "Once again, you promise me nothing bad will happen to those cats?" she asked cautiously.

"Hope to die."

"I wouldn't want you to die under any circumstances."

"Then you'll do it?"

"Well, we'll see," Pamela said warily. "Don't look so cocksure, Sammy. I only mean I'll think about it."

But where Pamela proved easy to handle, Henry offered difficulties. The younger boy came up to bed shortly after supper. "I shan't be able to go to sleep for hours," he announced nastily.

But Sam had been thinking furiously about this precise emergency. "You want to play a new game, Henry?" he asked blandly.

"What game?"

"Catfish."

"Don't know how to play it."

"It's easy," Sam said. "You just hold your breath. Whoever holds his breath the longest wins."

"What does he win?"

"What would you like to win?"

"The two books you got last Christmas." Sam nodded readily, and Henry's eyes grew suspicious. "What if I don't win?"

"Then you lose."

"What do I lose?"

"The guinea hen Pa promised to buy you."

"What would you do with that hen?"

"Sell it," Sam said honestly.

Henry's mind debated the stakes. He preferred the books to a hen he hadn't yet received and might never get. Moreover, even if he lost, he always had the chance of winning back the hen or bribing Sam to give it back or coaxing Ma into forcing Sam to surrender it. "All right," Henry said, "I'll sit right here on the bed and play."

"You'll do no such thing," Sam replied stormily. "Whoever heard of a catfish sitting up? We lie down on the bed."

"When do we start?"

Stretched beside Henry on the bed, Sam cried, "*Now!*"

Sam counted to himself as he held his breath. He reached twenty and glanced at Henry. The younger boy, resembling a blowfish out of water, seemed distressingly serene. At thirty Henry's cheeks were still puffed out in triumph. At forty Sam's temples began to pound. His skin felt damp and hot. He looked sharply at Henry and thought hopefully that the younger boy's face had started to turn a shade purple.

"Forty-one . . . forty-two . . ." Each number was becoming a labor, almost an agony for Sam, who felt that if he didn't exhale pretty soon, he'd burst. At fifty Henry's countenance was assuming a ghastly color. Sam felt encouraged. Maybe at fifty-five Henry would pass out. But at fifty-five Henry held on, eyes shut tight, mouth looking as though it belonged on a corpse, fists clenched in devilish determination. Sam could last no longer. He sounded like a gauge cock on a steamboat as the pent-up breath exploded from his lungs.

"The books are mine," Henry announced weakly.

Sam shook his head. "Only the first one!"

"You didn't say—"

"Yes, I did. I remember clearly. We'd play for one book at a time."

Henry's eyes narrowed. "I held my breath longer than you. I can do it again."

The frightful part of it all, Sam thought with a sinking heart, was the fact that Henry probably could.

3.

Mostly About Cats

HENRY SAT UP, curls swirling jauntily around his shoulders, and resumed his irritating singsong. "All right, Sammy. What are you waiting for? If you don't let me win that other book, I'll tell Ma!"

Sam cringed. Any secret respect that he had gained for the power of Henry's lungs was swept away by the humiliation of being bested by his younger brother. Shucks, Orion would have been easier to beat!

Feeling as though he had trapped himself, Sam wondered if Henry would like to play another game, and on the spur of the moment Sam invented Hangman. Two brothers tied bedsheets to the window and around their necks. They counted three and jumped. The one who lived the longer won. Sam wished he could really risk that game with Henry; then, blighting his pleasant reverie, Henry renewed his chant: "Come on, Sammy. You know I'll win. Ma told me how you were a sickly baby. I can hold my breath lots longer than you can."

This derisive challenge was more than Sam could bear. "Come on," he commanded in a surly voice.

Henry flung himself prone on the bed, his cheeks puffed out and his eyes closed tight in his fierce resolution to win.

"Go," Sam shouted. Suddenly his face broke into a grin. What luck! As long as Henry didn't open his eyes, Sam didn't have to hold his own breath. Sam guessed that it was not for nothing that, shortly before he was born, Halley's comet had passed across the sky, dragging a tail of fire so long that some folks thought it was the end of the world. Most people were satisfied to say that they were born under a lucky star, but Sam could claim a whole blooming comet!

Sam again kept count, and this time when he reached the number forty he felt a slight uneasiness. Henry didn't look good. Before, he had seemed purple; now he looked greenish. Perhaps it was only a trick of the fading twilight.

The count went to fifty, to sixty, to seventy. Sam had to admit it: Henry was a marvel! Like a clockmaker examining a fine watch, Sam studied his brother. The pulses in the other boy's temples were pounding furiously. Sweat larded Henry's face and neck. His chest seemed to swell. And Sam couldn't deny the color any longer. Henry's face was definitely green.

"He's doing fine," Sam reflected jovially. Maybe Henry would make one hundred and then explode. But at the count of eighty-six the tortured Henry finally gasped for breath. He lay on the bed, panting hard, too tired even to notice Sam's telltale composure.

"That makes us even," Sam announced cheerfully. "Want to try again?"

"Wanna go to sleep," Henry murmured miserably, rolling against the wall.

"Come on. You'll do better next time."

"In—the—morning—I'll—" Henry's voice drifted off, and Sam's grin widened. The younger boy was asleep in a wink.

Scarcely had darkness settled over Hannibal when from beneath the window Tom raised his muffled call. Sam scrambled out on the roof and dropped to the ground beside his friend.

"Will and Gull will meet us down at Wildcat Corner," Tom said.

"What's up?"

"You get the cats?"

"They're in the old chicken house."

"How many?"

"Five or six."

"I've got three hid in a bag under a bush. Gull promised to get four and Will two. How many will that make?"

"Fourteen or fifteen."

"Whoo-oop!" Tom slapped his leg gleefully. "That should do it all right."

"Do what?"

"You'll see."

"You tell me now, or I'm not going."

"We'll take your old cats anyhow."

"I went to a heap of trouble for you," Sam growled, and he told Tom how he had invented the game of Catfish to outwit Henry.

Tom's attitude changed entirely. "Sam, that was smart."

"So what are we going to do with all these cats?"

The idea, Tom said, had come to him when he saw how many guests were staying overnight at the Western Star Tavern. "People are packed in there like flies," Tom declared. "They're assembling for a big revival meetin' tomorrer. Came on the afternoon steamer, and one was tootin' a horn like he thought he was Gabriel. They had Injun Joe totin' carpet-bags till his wig tipped sideways."

"What's that got to do with cats, Tom?"

"Can't you see? We put the cats into boxes with lids that will come off easy. Religious people always go to bed early; they're the dangdest breed that way. Then we sneak into the Western Star and leave a cat in a box in each room. Most of the doors don't lock, and if they do, we'll push the cats through the transoms. Pretty soon those cats will get out of the boxes, feeling mean about the whole thing. Nothing howls uglier'n a cat with its fur standin' up on its tail. One after another those boarders'll wake up, grab those cats and fling 'em out into the hall. Now if fourteen strange cats, meeting in the hall, can't start a fight that'll be heard clear over to St. Jo, then I'm . . ."

But Tom didn't have to finish. Sam had already thrown himself onto the grass, rolling over and over and holding his sides with laughter. "Tom! Oh, you wonderful Tom!" he gasped between spasms of mirth.

"Come on, come on," Tom ordered roughly. "Get the cats!"

"You get yours."

"I'll meet you at the corner. Shove off, Sam! Those religious people must be going to bed by now."

Sam, grateful for the full moon that stared down on Hannibal, made his way to the abandoned chicken house. For a moment his spirit chilled—suppose Pamela had failed him, and the cats weren't there? Then, opening the door, Sam gazed delightedly at five of the largest felines in the Clemens household. The boy scooped them into his arms and ran to the corner where Tom waited impatiently, a hissing, spitting chorus rising from the writhing bag slung over his shoulder.

"Suppose Will and Gull don't show up?" Sam asked.

"I reckon we got enough cats between us to start quite a ruckus."

A touch of the tenderheartedness that disturbed Pamela and her mother suddenly smote Sam. "Tom, do you think anything bad will happen to these cats?"

"A kick in the slats never hurt any cat!"

"It won't be any worse'n that?"

"By morning these cats will be right back where we found

them. A cat knows where it's fed. Shucks, a cat'll go to food like a Mississippi keelboatman'll travel a thousand miles to a bottle of likker!"

Reassured, Sam trudged happily down the hill beside Tom. The town of Hannibal was about to discover that, although there might be nothing new under the sun, there indeed was something new under the moon. In a way, this was hardly any discovery at all for Hannibal. A great deal more than Tom's "religious people" drifted into a self-respecting Mississippi River port on a Saturday evening.

Tonight Hannibal's three saloons were doing a roaring business. A frontier town worked hard and played hard and cussed hard. Its fist fights were catch-as-catch-can, its knife fights bloody, its duels hot-tempered; its bullies swaggered with chests thrown out to the point of popping their buttons; its card players slapped down four aces with a special violence that defied the devil to prove the dealer had hidden them up his sleeve. Sam, caught up by the festive spirit of a Saturday night, chuckled.

"Watch out for some dog," Tom warned. "A dog coming for those cats could knock everything a-skelter."

Luckily, they reached Wildcat Corner without meeting any such catastrophe. Will and Gull loitered in the shadows. A snap of Gull's big toe brought the conspirators together.

"You get the cats?" Tom asked.

"Right here," Gull answered.

"You figger most of those people at the Western Star have gone to bed?"

"Will looked the place over, just a bit ago. Lights were out in most of the rooms even then."

A deep, malicious chuckle filled Tom's throat. "Those revival meetings usually start at sunup. This one'll start a lot earlier!"

The four boys crept along the moonlit street, hugging

the shadows of buildings, trees, and hedges. Behind Will Bowen bumped a sack of boxes appropriated from the store-room of Selmes's emporium. Tom grunted with pleasure when, at the inn, he found the door through the kitchen was open. Only the moon watched the quartet of excited ragamuffins stuffing cats into boxes, holding down lids, stuffing more cats, puffing, and muffling agonized cries when claws raised welts along the length of a carelessly exposed hand.

Tom took command. "We've got to move fast. Gull, you and Will take the first floor. Sam and I'll go upstairs to the second."

"Where'll we meet afterward?"

"Right there under that old apple tree. If we climb into the branches, nobody'll see us."

Night had brought a cool, damp breeze along the Mississippi, but Sam found himself sweating none the less. At Tom's signal, boys, cats, and boxes disappeared inside the Western Star.

The deed was accomplished more easily than Sam had expected. These people were sure a snorin' breed; even the creaking of a door's hinges, or the sound of a box sliding into the room didn't seem to disturb them. Once or twice Sam heard grumbles in the darkness, or a snore that broke off into a whirr-*whoosh* before resuming its buzzsaw cadence. Only one door was locked, and they saved that room until last. "We better light out'n here the instant that box hits the floor," Sam hissed as Tom hoisted him onto his shoulders so he could reach the transom.

Suddenly, from the other end of the hall a female voice screamed. "Abner, Abner! There's something furry crawling over my face!"

And immediately after, an even shriller voice from across the hall yelped, "Thar's a bear cub in here!"

"Let go that box!" hissed Tom.

Sam shoved cat and box through the transom and leaped to the floor. By the time the two boys reached the head of the stairs, chaos had broken out behind them.

"Why in tarnation are you licking my ear, Mirandy?"

"There's a big snake in here!"

"A muskrat got in!"

"It's a wolf with green eyes!"

Tom almost split with laughter at the mingled shouts and screams. Sam, too, choked until the tears ran down his cheeks. "Give 'em time and one of 'em will swear it's an alligator!" Tom chortled in Sam's ear.

The surprise and dismay of the outcries changed to screams of comprehension and rage.

"Why, it's a dang old cat!"

"Light the lamp!"

"Look out. Its back is up. You'll get scratched."

"Open the door, and I'll fling this dang critter into kingdom come!"

In the distance a dog began to yip; then, by twos and threes, the yelping started. "The dogs'll come where their noses bring 'em," Tom said wisely. "Come on, let's get downstairs!"

Doors were opening and slamming all through the tavern now. Cats landed on all fours, marked one life off their allotted nine, turned with arched backs, caught sight of another feline equally outraged and nasty-minded, marked two or three more lives off the promised nine, and pitched into the fight. It was a magnificent brawl, and afterward Hannibal, Missouri, dated events by the night when the cats took over the Western Star Tavern.

"See that striped one spit," Sam exclaimed at the foot of the stairs. "Why, that's Ma's lap cat!"

"Not now it ain't," Tom cried hilariously. "Lookit that cat go!"

Hissing cats clawed, backed off, howled piteously. Down the stairs they came, bolting between Sam's legs and Tom's, with their rigid tails all but flashing sparks. The first of the town's dogs to reach the tavern began to bark insanely.

"Don't bother with the door," Sam shouted. "Go out the window!"

Meanwhile doors were reopening. Voices boomed in a new burst of fury.

"Get a broom!"

"Get a pail of water!"

"Get a gun!"

"Look out—here come those cats right back into the room!"

By the time Tom and Sam joined Will and Gull in the apple tree, the first dog had found its way into the kitchen. Others soon followed. The bedlam—dogs yipping, cats screeching, humans screaming and banging brooms and slamming doors—could now be heard the length of Hanni-bal's river front. Card games broke up, fist fights were suspended, saloons and stores emptied out their customers From all directions men came running, shouting, cussing That noise aroused the remainder of Hannibal's dogs. Every street heard their frantic braying as they converged on the tavern.

Astraddle a branch in the old apple tree, Sam cried ecstatically, "This is better'n a fire!"

4.

Stowaway

AFTER THE AFFAIR of the cats, Sam's good behavior endured for almost a month. Yet minor lapses occurred. On the night before Orion returned to St. Louis the preacher in Orion won out. Sam suffered through a long lecture, wriggling and biting his nails and wishing that by mistake Orion would sail on a slave ship for darkest Africa. Afterward he felt blue and mean, and if Henry had possessed any sense, he would not have picked that evening to taunt Sam in his squeaky, singsong voice.

"Sammy, I know you let out those cats at the Western Star."

"Oh, shut up!"

"Wait till I tell Ma."

"You better not."

"Give me those two books, or I will tell her."

Henry's threat, coming on top of Orion's lecture, was more than Sam could stand. He doubled up his fist and let fly, catching Henry squarely in the left eye. The younger boy's bellows were loud enough to shake windowpanes in houses a block away. Jane Clemens laced Sam's legs until they bled.

"It was worth it," Sam boasted to Tom. "You oughta see Henry's eye!"

"Real black-and-blue, eh?"

"Purple and puffy. You'd swear he'd collided with the paddle wheel of the *Jeanie Deans*.

"Had it coming to him," Tom said. "Bother with Henry. Let's go swimming."

Sam hesitated. "Ma said I wasn't to go—not for a week —because of what I did to Henry."

"Who's going to see us down to Bear Creek?" Tom scoffed. "No one but hog drovers."

It was wonderful swimming at Bear Creek. Tom, leaping high from a log and twisting his naked body in two complete loops before he struck the water, fancied himself the best diver in Hannibal. But Sam was Tom's equal and maybe better. The two boys were so engrossed in matching their prowess that they did not notice the approach of Tom's older brother Bence.

There was a mean streak in Bence. He was a large, lumbering, oafish fellow, dressed in rags every bit as disreputable as Tom's, whose idea of sport was to steal up on younger boys while they were swimming, soak their clothes, and leave the garments tightly knotted. When Tom and Sam finally realized he was there, he was already engaged in this dim-witted villainy.

Sam rushed at Bence like a tiger. "Get your dirty hands off'n my clothes!"

Bence threw back his head and roared with laughter. With one huge hand, the size of a ham hock, he could easily smother Sam's whole face. Today he preferred to embellish that trick. He caught Sam around the neck, tossed him over his shoulder, giving his spine a nasty twist, and heaved the boy through the air as though he were a dead pig in a sack. Sam crashed into Bear Creek with a titanic splash. Bence guffawed. Then he saw Tom coming for him with a club. Bence turned and fled, running like the wind.

"I'll kill you if you don't let decent folks alone," Tom shouted.

"Yah, yah, yah," Bence hooted over his shoulder.

Tom's feet skittered on the path, making the chase harder.

"You just keep away from me, Bence! I ain't taking no pushin' around from you or Pap!"

"Yah, yah, yah!" Bence answered.

Disgusted, Tom threw down the club and abandoned the hopeless pursuit.

Sam, on the verge of losing consciousness, was half-drowned before Tom found him. Tom hailed a wagon and took him home. What flabbergasted Jane Clemens most was the sight of Sammy riding stark naked through the streets of Hannibal. "Sammy, the neighbors will think we have no shame!"

"I could have died," the boy wailed in bounteous self-pity.

Jane Clemens sniffed. "A person born to be hanged is safe in the water."

But his mother's sharpness was only a pose. The thought that a serious accident could have befallen Sam appalled her, and she indulged the lad in many ways. With Orion in St. Louis, she moved Henry into his bed so that Sam could have a room to himself, a freedom that he craved. Sam enjoyed leaving the door open at night and listening to his parents talking in the kitchen.

Orion would have scolded Sam for eavesdropping—Orion always had a word that gave even a mean twist to the good hard sense of learning what was going on in the family. Sam didn't care. Lying there in the dark, hearing his father's heavy, ponderous voice ascend the stairs like notes from a pipe organ, his mind formed an image of the man.

Judge John Clemens—he wasn't really a judge, but a justice of the peace—was tall and spare, with piercing gray eyes under bushy hair that he brushed back vigorously, and with a mouth that, like Orion's, rarely smiled and never laughed. Sam supposed that his father possessed the power of life and death over all men and could hang any that offended him. It was no wonder he looked so stern and prim and determined, Sam thought. That was an awful power; if it were his, once he had disposed of Henry on the gallows and maybe hung Bence for almost drowning him, he'd want to wash his hands of it.

Years before—that is, before Sam had been born, a part of history that didn't count—his father had lived in Tennessee. He had bought a large tract of land there—75,000 acres by most accounts—and this "Tennessee land" was the subject about which Judge Clemens most enjoyed talking. Some day that land would make them all rich. Then everyone would know how smart he'd been, and how hard he had worked and planned and sacrificed to give his family a fine future.

"You'd think it was Orion talking, listening to him," Sam thought.

Sometimes Sam supposed that he was wrong for harboring his long bitterness against his father. Years had passed now since Jennie, the Clemens slave girl, had been sold. But Sam could still remember. He had adored Jennie; she had been his "mammy." If Jennie was sassy, so was Sam. Once when his father had whipped her, the boy had felt as if every lash struck him, too.

Ma said that they had to sell Jennie, because they needed the money so badly. When Sam learned the truth about the sale he had stormed into the room where his father sat placidly reading the paper.

"You sold her down the river," Sam cried piteously. "You sold her to a slave trader who will put her on a plantation. They'll beat her and kick her and work her to death!"

Judge Clemens lowered his newspaper. "I did what I had

to, Sammy," he said quietly. "I'll not discuss the matter any further."

Afterward Sam had sobbed. His grief for Jennie lasted for weeks, and he thoroughly disliked Sandy, the little Negro boy whom shortly thereafter his father bought to help Ma around the house. No boy the size of a peanut could replace Sam's beloved Jennie, least of all one who sang at the top of his voice all day long. Sam complained bitterly to Ma.

"Make him stop. He gives me a headache."

Jane Clemens shook her head. "Think, Sammy. He is sold away from his mother, who lives in Maryland—a thousand miles from here. He will never see her again, poor thing. When he is singing, he is not grieving. The noise he makes drives me crazy, too, but I'm always grateful for it. Should Sandy ever stop singing, it would break my heart."

Sam hadn't argued any more. Sandy had drawn him closer to Ma. And straitened finances, an old story with the Clemenses, soon forced the Judge also to sell Sandy, the last slave he would ever bring home to Hannibal.

Like ghosts out of the night these reflections flitted across Sam's mind as through the darkness he strained to overhear the conversation in the kitchen.

"We've got to have some money," Ma said.

"There isn't much law business right now," the Judge grumbled.

"I can't go on owing poor Mr. Selmes forever," Ma insisted.

"We'll have to sell something."

"What? We'll soon be eating off the floor with borrowed spoons as it is."

A pause followed, then the Judge spoke again. "I guess I'll have to sell the Tennessee land." His tone was as sorrowful as if he were agreeing to wrench off his right arm.

"If anybody'll buy it."

Sam sucked in his breath. He had heard Pa fly off the handle before, when Ma said that. Tonight the tense silence dragged on; finally, the Judge arose and walked heavily across the floor and out the kitchen door.

Sleep came fretfully to Sam. It wasn't finding food to eat that worried him—shucks, he and Tom could always manage that—but he would have liked a little ready cash for another scheme that had been growing in his mind.

Summer had crept down the old Mississippi, ripening the red haws and persimmons, the hickory nuts and walnuts. What would make this summer the best in his life if it wasn't to sail down the river on the *Jeanie Deans?* With Sam today's impulse was tomorrow's command. Wishes grew into necessities. Within a week he reckoned that there wasn't much point in living less'n he made that trip. He began making plans.

Tom, Will, and Gull soon noticed how secretive and standoffish Sam had become. When old John Hannicks shouted, "Steeammm-*boat* a-comin'," and the long legs and short legs raced dogs, drays, and carts down the hill to the dock, Sam took to acting queer.

"What are you doin', off by yourself as if'n you can't stand the stink of us?" Tom demanded.

"I'm thinking."

"No wonder you look sick."

"He's coming down with the fever," Gull declared. "Or the milksick."

"Maybe he's got a girl," Will snickered.

"Both's as bad," Tom said. "Thinking's sure to spoil the best of us. We oughta pitch him in the river and let the paddle wheel knock some sense into his head."

Sam didn't care what they said. Planning to be a stowaway aboard the *Jeanie Deans* required time and patience. Afterward, when he had been to Memphis or Natchez or maybe even New Orleans, they'd have to look up to him and admit that, although George Washington was the father of the country, the slickest thing ever seen in Missouri was Sam Clemens!

Friday was the best day for stowing away, Sam decided. Friday marked the pilot's last trip before his day off, and he was always eager to get home to his wife and younguns. The *Jeanie Deans* barely rubbed her bow against the dock at Hannibal before she was off again. Everything was tumbled onto the deck—cargo, passengers, luggage. In the confusion of drays and rearing horses, old ladies waving their parasols for Injun Joe to fetch their carpetbags, and deck hands cussing the dogs for chewing the hawser ropes, nobody would notice Sam slipping aboard. Off the main cabin was a lifeboat, just made to hide under. Shucks, he could do it easy!

For two nights before the chosen day, Sam tossed in bed, glad Henry wasn't there to badger him with questions as he worked over his plan. Friday brought humid mists and an overcast sky, but an excited Sam ignored these forbidding signs. He dressed early, ate dutifully, and was especially careful not to arouse Ma's umbrage. Long before even John Hannicks thought to look, Sam was at the dock, watching for the first smudge of smoke beyond the point. The humid weather, the gray skies hung on. Tempers generally seemed short and rough. But not Sam's—his heart sang.

As the *Jeanie Deans* drew closer to shore, the pilot appeared, barking at the deck hands as soon as he stepped out of his glass-enclosed cabin. There won't be any loitering today, Sam thought gaily. That pilot wants to get home! He'll chuck the passengers off the boat and the cargo and luggage with them. The confusion would almost equal that of the night when the cats had taken over the Western Star Tavern. Sam, knowing he must avoid Tom, Will, and Gull, hid behind a pile of skids. The gauge cocks screamed; the bell clanged; the heavy, moist air drove clouds of black smoke down onto the docks; the gangplank slammed into place.

"Here's where I git," Sam muttered. He bumped against Injun Joe, but the Osage grunted and said nothing as he watched the boy scramble over the deck rail. Quick as a fox squirrel, Sam ducked under the lifeboat. Injun Joe shrugged and walked away.

Sam's heart pounded mightily. He clung to the deck, waiting, trembling, cheek pressed flat against the boards, while the pilot shouted imprecations at the crew:

"Shake the lead, you chicken-hearted loafers. We've already wasted one bell on this stinking hole. Move, drat your worthless, lazy hides. Don't tangle that rope! Heave that crate, and if the old woman don't want to move, she danged soon will. *Where* you going with that barrel, you crazy split between a mud turtle and crippled hearse horse? Move, *move*, get that gangplank up, you egg-sucking, sheep-stealing son of a stuffed turkey! Drown the dog if he won't get off. H'ist up the steam. Mate, unglue your fingers and ring the bell. Next time we'll skip this whole broken-down hog-callers' paradise. Ain't fit to be seen except on a murky night, anyhow!"

Sam had never heard such a marvelous flow of words. There simply wasn't any greater majesty on earth than to be able to stand on the hurricane deck and peal out such wonderful insults. The crew worked themselves into a lather. In less than four minutes the *Jeanie Deans* steamed away from Hannibal.

The pilot swore at such rotten handling of a boat. The crew was eight seconds off the record.

As soon as open water showed between boat and dock, Sam began to breathe easier. Another bell clanged, the

Jeanie Deans back paddled, shivered from stem to stern, then chugged ahead with a har*rumph*-thump, har*rumph*-thump. Serenity came back to the deck, for the pilot had returned to his cabin to think out the abuse he would hurl at the town of Louisiana, his next stop. Sam reckoned he was safe for a spell, but just then two deck hands came over and leaned against the lifeboat. For some minutes they treated Sam to a spirited, profane debate over whether the pilot was descended from a family of Missouri mud hens or a long line of Arkansas jackasses.

Thereafter Sam's education advanced by leaps and bounds. Originally, when the world was created, there were three classes of liars. First were the small-sized fibbers, who told little white lies, usually to spare the feelings of others. Next came the medium-sized liars, with romance in their hearts, who dreamed that life was a lot better than its everyday, humdrum pattern indicated. Finally, there were the professional liars, who told whoppers to serve their own shady purposes, and spent half their lifetimes trying to remember what they had said to whom and where and why. Even so, along in the early 1800's, whoever it was that made liars decided that he hadn't done his level best and so he created Mississippi boatmen, the biggest liars of all.

Ed and Mike belonged to this breed. Sometimes they lied just to keep in practice, as when Ed said, "I lost a thousand dollars in that poker game in Natchez."

"Where'd you get a thousand dollars?"

"Stole it from the pilot."

"Where'd he get it?"

"Stole it from me."

"Why didn't you report him?"

"I stole it from him before that."

And sometimes they lied just to be mean and to strike

back at the world in general, as when Mike said, "They're going to sell this boat."

"How do you know?"

"Heard the new owner talking to the pilot when we laid over in Cincinnati."

"What'd he pay for her?"

"More'n she's worth. Worse yet, he's going to let the whole crew go when we reach St. Louie."

"Dash-dang if we shouldn't walk off her at the next port then."

"I'll do it."

"So will I."

"Let the pilot see how he likes to load her and stoke her and steer her."

"Good idea."

Sam, who had no notion of how fast and fancy-free the two deck hands were playing with the truth, wondered fretfully what would happen to the *Jeanie Deans* when the pilot was left to manage her by himself. Meanwhile he failed to notice how much darker the day had grown, how much uglier the sky, until a few large drops of water splattered the deck. Then suddenly the heavens opened, and rain poured down in torrents. A cold wind swept up the river, shook the *Jeanie Deans,* and finding Sam, chilled to the bone under the lifeboat, shook him, too. The boy sneezed explosively. Ed and Mike, who had retired to the engine room doorway, heard the sneeze, and investigated. Each grabbed a leg, and Sam slid out like a flounder on a chopping board.

"What'd you call it, Ed?"

"Human, I guess."

"Shall we heave him to the fishes?"

"Might save him and use him for bait down river. Some of those big catfish bite good on small boys."

Sam finally managed to struggle to his feet, and tried to shake off the iron clasp of Mike's hand. "You leave go'n me!"

"Maybe you better cat 'n' nine tail him," Ed suggested.

"Hangin's better," Mike said.

Sam shivered as a wave of fear curled the tips of his toes, yet he sassed back, "You touch me, an' my father'll hang you!"

"Will he now?" asked Ed, real pleased. "And who's your pap?"

"A judge!"

"So's Mike—a jedge of bad likker!" Ed was so filled with glee at his own joke that he almost fell into the engine room.

"Where you from?" Mike demanded.

"Hannibal."

"Hannibal!" Mike spat as though to clean the word out of his mouth. "That's a rotten hole. No wonder they named it after a defeated general."

Ed laughed so that he all but fell into the engine room again, but Sam failed to understand that he was being initiated into one of the hoariest jokes known to Mississippi travelers.

"What's your name?" Mike asked, his fierce look not quite hiding the twinkle in his eye.

"Clemens. Sam Clemens."

"Dash-dang silly name. Whyn't you change it?"

"Maybe I will some day."

"Right pert little sass-box, ain't you?"

"I ain't afraid."

"I ain't brung you to the pilot, yet," Mike said sinisterly. This time Ed laughed so hard that he did fall into the engine room. Mike left him there. "Come along with you," he ordered, slipping a hand under Sam's collar and yanking the boy till his tongue hung out. "I ain't rightfully sure what the pilot'll do to you, but whatever it is it won't be good!"

Sam remembered that fearful man, commanding from the hurricane deck when the *Jeanie Deans* had docked at Hannibal. Suddenly his mouth tasted bad and his legs began to tremble. "You make him go easy," he begged Mike.

"Me? I can't stop him if'n he takes a mind to slit your throat with a knife."

"He won't!"

"An ax is a lot cleaner. Gets the job over quicker, too."

By the time Mike dragged a frightened, quivering Sam into the pilot's cabin the rain had soaked both of them. Two more disreputable specimens of humanity were not imaginable. The pilot looked at Sam, cussed for three minutes, looked again at Sam, cussed two minutes more, and then asked in a civil voice, "You got relatives in the next port?"

A cowed Sam nodded meekly.

The pilot chewed his mustache for a spell. "You're a danged fool to stow away on a day like this," he said.

"I didn't think it'd rain, sir."

"It *always* rains when the birds sit sluggish on the deck pilings," the pilot said with a rumble of thunder in his scorn. "Nobody in Hannibal amounts to anything, an' you're as useless as the rest. Ought to throw you overboard, but I suppose a rat like you wouldn't drown. So instead I'll have you thrown off the boat at the next stop, and your folks can drive you back to Hannibal."

Sam blinked back the tears, thinking of the humiliation this journey promised.

"Ain't you going to do nothing to him?" Mike asked maliciously.

While Sam quaked in his shoes, the pilot gazed down at him. Finally, he nodded his head. "Give him the usual treatment."

"You better not hurt me," cried Sam, his spunkiness rallying once more. "My Pa's a judge, and he'll hang . . ."

The pilot waved his hand, not even listening. "Take him down to the ladies' lounge. Let them cuddle the poor little rain-soaked lamb and fuss over him so that he won't miss his Mamma and douse him with hot tea so he won't catch a cold. If that doesn't cure him of running away, nothin' will!"

"Aye," Mike said.

Sam was staggered by this fiendish, unexpected punishment. He cringed, admitting the awful, diabolical cleverness of the pilot. All at once he was struggling to hold back tears the size of raindrops. What bitter calamity had come to Sam Clemens on this day when he had intended to share a place in history beside George Washington!

5.

On the Farm

T HE NIGHT a bedraggled Sam was brought home as an
apprehended stowaway Jane Clemens decided that the
family would spend the rest of the summer on her brother's
farm near Florida, Missouri. If this was meant as further punishment for Sam, Mrs. Clemens was certainly tempering dis-
cipline with mercy. To Sam's mind, a summer on his uncle's
farm was next best to a summer on a Mississippi steamboat.

"Sammy," his mother told him, "I *think* there's a good
side in you as well as this streak of the devil. Anyhow, as
your Ma, I have to hope so. Otherwise I wouldn't be fretting every time there's a measles scare or a milksick scare
for fear you won't live. I'd be worrying instead that you
would!"

"I just want to have fun."

"I know." When Jane Clemens smiled suddenly and
brushed back her hair with a swift, gay gesture, anyone
could see why she had once been called a beauty. "When
I was growing up," she confessed, "—and I was a girl once,
Sammy, back in Kentucky and Tennessee—fun was what
I thought about. I adored dancing, and during the whole
week from Christmas to New Year's I'd ride off on horse-
back to dances. I'd dance all night to the music of one or

two violins, sleep a little, and dance all day at the next house. I scandalized some folks just as you do, but I never meant any harm." The woman laughed. "Somewhere in heaven an angel must have shelled two peas from the same pod, and you and I fell out, both of us with the same wild impulses!"

Sam had never heard Ma talk like this, as though she didn't really blame him for wanting so badly to ride on the *Jeanie Deans* that he had run away. What was the matter with Ma? This was no way for a grownup to act, as though she wished she were still young and free and harum-scarum.

Jane Clemens herself wondered if she had spoken wisely. "We're going to the farm because it'll do you good to get out of Hannibal for a spell," she continued, with an effort at a frown. "Nobody knows what will drift down that river next—thieves and cardsharps and worthless do-nothings like the Blankenships. If a boy turns out bad, most would blame his Ma and Pa, but I'll tell you what, Sammy—I'd lay the blame right at the door of that wicked old river!"

Sam possessed the good sense not to argue with Ma when she tilted her chin and looked at him with her steady blue eyes. Anyhow, his mind now was full of going to the farm. He'd see Puss, his favorite cousin. Down in the slave quarters, he'd see Uncle Dan'l and poor old crippled, bedridden Aunt Nell who claimed she was more than a thousand years old and had once talked to Moses. He'd ride the mules in the fields, and eat watermelons, and scare his aunt by curling a live snake in her sewing basket, a prank that never failed. And there would be Mary, the slave always delegated to watch over Puss and him. Sam chuckled. Mary wasn't much older than they were; she aided rather than hindered their mischief.

All that night Sam could hardly sleep, thinking how

grand it would be to visit Aunt Patsy and Uncle John Quarles. Yet one uneasy association with the farm came back, involving Pa's absent-mindedness. One summer Ma started ahead for the farm with the other children, leaving Pa to fetch Sam. The Judge simply forgot, riding off without his son, and Uncle John had saddled a horse and ridden the poor beast into a lather to rescue Sammy, who had felt lonely and bewildered over the whole affair and waited for something to happen while he poked his finger into a sack and watched the grain spill out of the hole.

Other memories arose in Sam's mind. He loved the old farmhouse and, most of all, the family room with a trundle bed in one corner and a spinning wheel in another.

Nothing ever sounds so mournful, Sam thought, as the rising and falling wail of that wheel! It was like listening to the spirits of the dead. He never felt melancholy or homesick until the wheel began to spin, but then, no matter how hard Puss tried to cheer him, he always wanted to crawl off somewhere, to curl up, to cry.

He remembered the huge fireplace, piled high with logs whose sugary sap bubbled out the ends and was good to scrape off and eat. He remembered the lazy cat stretched out on the rough hearthstones, and the dogs blinking drowsily as they braced against the doorjambs, and his uncle sucking on a corncob pipe and resting his legs on a splint-bottom chair. Sam sighed happily and fell into contented slumber.

He told Tom next day he was going away for the rest of the summer.

"What do I care?" Tom's sudden, harsh surliness was like a lash across the face.

"Tom, don't you think I'll miss you?"

"Not much."

"But I will!"

"Well, I won't miss you. Don't bother to come back for all I care."

Sam couldn't understand Tom's ugliness.

"She's the one," Tom broke out with quickening rage. "Your Ma. She wants to be rid of the likes of me."

"I don't."

"You won't say *she* don't."

"Ma can think her way, and I can think mine," Sam said with spirit, his cheeks flushing.

"She'll turn you around."

"No, she won't."

"You wouldn't swear to it."

"Yes, I would."

"In blood?"

"In blood."

Tom rummaged through his pockets and found the rusty knife he used for scaling catfish. "Not much you won't," he dared Sam, pushing it toward him.

Sam gritted his teeth. His arm trembled as, lips thrust out in a determined pout, he pricked the middle finger of his left hand and squeezed out four drops of blood. "There," he cried triumphantly. "I swear it!"

Tom still scowled as he returned the knife to his pocket. His sulky voice threatened, "See that you keep it, or Bence and me'll fix you good!" Abruptly, Tom turned on his heel and fled down the hill, leaving Sam to stare after him.

Jane Clemens saw the bloody smear on his shirt and asked, "How'd you cut yourself, Sammy?"

"Nail, I guess." A touch of Tom's surliness had crept into his own voice. All through the morning Sam felt depressed. He was blue and angry in a way he could neither explain nor resist.

That afternoon the Clemenses drove off to the farm. As the wagon jolted along, Sam glared down at the cut finger. "I swore it, and I'll keep it," he muttered, still feeling a deep, inexplicable unhappiness.

Tom watched them go from behind the tumble-down barn on the premises where the Blankenships claimed squatter's rights. He could see the Clemenses without their seeing him. Nobody ever would see Tom Blankenship cry, either. Then, remembering how Bence had almost drowned Sam that morning at Bear Creek, Tom picked up a club and went in search of his older brother. He hunted Bence until nightfall, but this was one of those times when Bence disappeared for days.

Two miles out of Hannibal, Sam could stand it no longer. "I wish Tom could have come!" he blurted out.

"It's right to miss a friend, Sammy," said his mother.

"You don't like Tom."

"I don't know him as you do. Maybe you see more in people than I do."

Without his knowing why, going off to the farm for the summer became fun again for Sam.

With a shout, Uncle John Quarles greeted the Clemens family, now travel-worn, dusty, and filled with the irritabilities of a long journey. Compared to Judge Clemens' owlish solemnity, Uncle John was still a boy who, although he had grown older, had never lost his energy or enthusiasm or innate prankishness. He lifted Jane Clemens from the wagon, whirled her around with skirts flying, and set her down in the grass with a laugh. He tickled Pamela until she giggled wildly, thrust a stick of licorice into Henry's gaping, awestruck mouth, and then turned to Sam.

"You've grown two inches," Uncle John shouted. "You've put some flesh on those scrawny bones, but we'll fatten you up more—boys and hogs are what we handle best on this farm. Puss, Puss! Where is that imp of a girl? For days she's been moping around waiting for Sammy to get here, and now she's disappeared like a spider down a mouse hole!"

Puss, standing right behind him, laughed gaily at her father's bubbling spirits, and Aunt Patsy, taking off the apron that she would put back on the next instant, reprimanded, "John, there never was an empty barrel made as much clatter as you. I declare!"

Sam thought he would burst out of his skin with happiness. In sudden ecstasy, he capered around the yard with his arms swinging and exploded into a series of somersaults. Judge Clemens shook his head at his excitable, impetuous son, but the others laughed. Then everyone tramped into the double log house where the table groaned under the weight of platters of fried chicken, roast pig, pheasant, and a dozen other steaming dishes prepared by Aunt Hanner, the Negro cook.

With Puss in tow, Sam spent the first day rediscovering the farm—the barns, the corncribs, the tobacco house, the brook, the swings in the pasture that hung by 40-foot ropes from the branches of walnut trees, the meadows sparkling with clover and throbbing with the music of singing grasshoppers and calling larks. They ate blackberries in the fence rows, visited the apple orchards and the horses and ox teams in the stables, watched prairie chickens scurry from sight, the cows that moved up the hillside jingling their bells, and the snakes sunning themselves along the dusty roads. Throughout the long, joyous exploration, hawks hung motionless in the blue sky overhead as though deciding whither to spread the message that Sam Clemens had returned.

In 1843, the people in this part of Missouri looked upon slavery as a benevolent institution. The Quarleses, like the Clemenses, were Southern in their "long talk," habits, and viewpoint. Down in the Quarters, where the Quarles Negroes lived, none disagreed with Uncle Dan'l's estimate that John Quarles was "a good Massa, de best." Year in, year out, there was no change in Uncle Dan'l except that his wrinkled old face grew gentler, his dark eyes more kindly, his big heart more loyal, his childlike faith in human goodness deeper.

"Whoo-oops, hyar's dat Sammy," cried Uncle Dan'l, flinging out his arms as though welcoming an angel from heaven.

Sam's heart bounded. His first love on the farm was the Quarters; his favorite among all living mortals, Uncle Dan'l. Boy and slave joined hands, heads thrown back in glee, kicking up the dust as they danced around, sending the geese flying, the other children screaming, the dogs barking.

"Boy, how you's growed!" Uncle Dan'l cackled.

"Will you take me hunting?"

"'Spects Ah will!"

"When?"

"'Most sooner'n you 'spects."

The Quarters had its own rigid code of etiquette, and any first visit demanded a call upon poor old bedridden Aunt Nell, who tied her thin white tufts of woolly hair with thread to ward off the spell of witches. Sam stood between Puss and Uncle Dan'l and gazed with wide, respectful eyes at this wheezing old lady who knew how to prevent cramps with snake rattles and could banish ghosts by making the sign of the cross. Looking up at Sam, her withered old lips broke into a smile. "Sammy, you ain't forgot dis tired ole woman?"

"I'm never going to forget you, Aunt Nell," Sam answered with honest feeling.

"Dat's good, Sammy. Ah fixes a potion. You's safe no matter whut if'n you jest 'members ole Aunt Nell's a-lookin' out!"

"I will, I will!"

Aunt Nell sighed. It was a powerful hard business, she complained, to live more than a thousand years. Folks who read their Bibles knew all she'd been through. As a young girl she had talked to Moses. She hadn't rightfully felt perky, Aunt Nell declared, since she had lost her health in the desert, coming out of Egypt. The old lady asked Sam to bend over and look at the bald spot on her head. Did Sammy know what had caused that?

"It was the fright you felt seeing Pharaoh drown," the boy said, for he had heard the story many times.

Aunt Nell nodded happily. Sammy was a good boy because he 'membered. Everyone in the Quarters believed Aunt Nell's stories, just as they believed in her powers of black magic and swore that when Uncle Dan'l suffered his occasional fits of lockjaw it was because Aunt Nell had grown peevish and cast a spell. Sam, always a prudent respecter of superstitions, played safe by treating with credulity everything that Aunt Nell's toothless gums said and claimed.

The days of summer rushed by. Tramping off through the fields with Uncle Dan'l, Sam learned a lore of nature he would never forget. Since animals didn't know right from wrong, Uncle Dan'l believed that they all went to heaven. Animals didn't bother over how a body smelled— animals just went on about their business, no matter—and animals were smart.

"Now lookit dere." Uncle Dan'l chuckled. "You see dat ole turkey hen? She make out she's been wounded. See dere, how she limp? She do dat, boy, an' leave you foller her fo' miles till she wear you out or lose you."

"Let's not shoot her, Uncle Dan'l."

"Ain't none ob 'em Ah laks to shoot 'cept mebbe a coon or a possum to shet up de crazy dogs."

Gray squirrels and fox squirrels watched the old slave and

the boy trudging through the woods. Chickens, pecking around the granary, looked curiously at the pair and then lunged back at the ground. Snakes were a separate science under Uncle Dan'l's tutelage, and he taught Sam how to recognize the places where puff adders and rattlers were most likely to lurk. There wasn't nothing to hoop snakes, Uncle Dan'l declared. Puss squirmed as Sam held up a garter snake and let its fangs dart against his fingers.

Puss lived in constant awe of Sam. She followed him like a slave. The brook ran deep, dark, and quiet beside the tobacco house. Here was a forbidden swimming hole, and so Sam would swim nowhere else.

"Sammy, we shouldn't."

"Then you stay behind."

"Oh, Sammy—you're an awful sinner."

"The best since Adam," Sam boasted. "Me and Tom. You don't know Tom, but, believe me, he's a wonderful sinner."

Uncle Dan'l sat in the shade of the tobacco house, telling no one he was there, not even Sam. Watching the fancy dives Sam achieved while Puss cried out in admiration, Uncle Dan'l shook his head. "Dat boy," the old man muttered, "is got somepin bottled up in him an' no notion ob how to git it out. Lookit dat boy fly—lak a bird. De Lawd should've give Sammy wings; he'd a-knowed how to use 'em!"

Biscuits, batter cakes, corn pone, boiled corn, succotash, tomatoes, peas, Irish potatoes, milk, clabber, melons, pies— Aunt Hanner stuffed Sam that summer, determined to hog- fatten him.

September brought harvest time, and the oxen, harnessed and trodding endlessly in a circle, threshed the wheat into grain while Sam darted between their legs and climbed onto their backs. Uncle Dan'l clamped tight his eyes, sure

the boy would be trampled into pulp, but Jane Clemens said placidly, "I don't think the Lord intended for Sammy to die that way!"

Down in the Quarters, Sam sat with knees under his chin, leaning against Uncle Dan'l's shoulder and listening to the Negroes singing spirituals. One day Aunt Nell surprised him, turning around with a lighted candle stuck in her mouth, and cackled with glee when he jumped a foot. Sam tried the same prank on Henry, who howled with fright. When night came, the family gathered around the fire. Hickory wood popped, and the tall eight-day clock in the corner ticked as regularly as old Aunt Nell wheezed. Sam drowsed off, watching the reflections from the fire dancing on the barrels of the deer guns over the mantelpiece.

The summer had raced away from them, and when, one night toward mid-September, Aunt Patsy worked her spinning wheel, the mournful sound stirred mixed emotions in

Sam. Soon he would be leaving the farm till next summer, a thought that filled him with melancholy. But then, quickly, he grew homesick for Hannibal and the old river and the good times skylarking with Will and Tom and Gull. The pledge he had sealed in blood with Tom had not been forgotten. "He'll see," Sam muttered. "Sometimes he's too smart for his pants, Tom is."

On Sundays horses were hitched to the big wagon and the Quarleses and the Clemenses drove the three and a half miles to services at the village church in Florida. Sam liked the hymn-singing. He speculated from the chink of the small silver how much should be in the collection plate, and dozed through the long sermon or kept Puss giggling by catching imaginary flies. The church at Florida was constructed of logs with a puncheon floor and slab benches. It also had fleas, enough to rouse the drowsiest worshiper into short spells of respectful, itchy wakefulness. The church was cool, even on the hottest summer days, and Sam, staring down through the floor chinks, was delighted to discover the hogs that slept there. It was not until after the evening when Sam began to think again of Tom and Hannibal that those slumbering hogs popped into his everyday reveries.

That Saturday Sam sought out Uncle Dan'l in the Quarters. "You lend me two hound dogs, Uncle Dan'l?"

"You gwine possum huntin', boy?"

"I need those dogs."

"Uh-huh," Uncle Dan'l said wisely, "an' you ain't sayin' why. You is up to somepin, Sammy—whut Ah can't say 'cause Ah don't know. Dogs is where they always is. If you take 'em, sooner or later dey come back. Ah'll see 'em when dey do!"

Sam grinned. Uncle Dan'l was the finest kind of conspirator, since he didn't ask questions. Young Mary, the slave who was supposed to be a sort of guardian to Sam, proved more troublesome.

"How come, Sammy, you want me to walk dem hound dogs all de way to Florida?"

"I need 'em."

"What fo'?"

"Lookit," Sam said, rather crossly, "all you have to do is bring those dogs and then watch the window by the church door. When I wave a handkerchief, you let those dogs loose under the church floor."

"Will Ah get whupped fo' dis, Sammy?"

"Not if you high-tail it home."

"Can't Ah hide in de bushes an' watch?"

"Well, a little while," Sam said, "but you better not let Uncle Dan'l miss you too long."

"He ain't gwine to whup me."

"Or let anyone else do it, silly—that's the point."

Sunday was a magnificent day, and the Quarleses and the Clemenses drove off to church in good spirits. If Sam seemed a bit flushed of face, Jane Clemens attributed it to the normal excitement any form of movement induced in the lad. The summer had worked wonders with Sammy, Jane Clemens thought—it had fattened him, calmed down his high animal spirits, curbed his runaway imagination. Judge Clemens glanced at Sam somewhat uneasily. Whenever the boy looked angelic, the Judge remembered that the most hardened criminals were often those who looked as though they had been running an errand for their mothers when, unfortunately, temptation overtook them.

The services that Sabbath followed the usual pattern—hymn-singing, prayer, hymn-singing, the collection, and then the sermon that started off under a low head of steam as though it didn't expect to reach its destination until about two o'clock that afternoon. Henry fell asleep and the Judge nudged him forcibly. Like Aunt Nell, the preacher seemed to have suffered from the fright of watching Pharaoh drown, and had difficulty finding the right words to which he could attach a "hem" or a "haw" or an "ah."

Sam stared down at the puncheon floor, grinning. Slowly, he worked the handkerchief out of his pocket. While Ma and Pa stared straight ahead in bug-eyed concentration, while Uncle John scratched a flea and Aunt Patsy scowled at Puss for giggling, Sam bounced up. He flipped the handkerchief toward the window and waved vigorously.

Sam heard the hound dogs scurrying under the floor. Wait till they find those hogs, he thought, tense with happy excitement. The preacher droned along.

"Then Moses-*haw* beheld a vision-*hem* and a voice said-*ah* . . ."

But nobody ever heard what the voice told Moses. The dogs had found the hogs. Growls and squeals rose in frightful crescendo . . . and into Sam's mind leaped an image of one glorious tangle of dogs and hogs whirling round and round in a frenzied circle.

Feet jerked up as though the snaps and bites and growls and squeals were coming straight through the puncheon floor. Young Henry threw back his head and howled. A hog emerged into the sunlight, its back bristling like a porcupine. A hound dog followed, snapping viciously. Round the log church went dog and prey, ripping away the Sabbath sanctity with fearful abandon. The horses tied to the trees reared and whinneyed shrilly. Aunt Patsy's face drained of all color, but Uncle John said with great animation, "Most wide-awake service we've had in ten years!"

Sam hoped that Mary had high-tailed it for home, as he had told her. Under his feet the bloodthirsty battle between canine and swine still buckled the floor.

Riding home, Judge Clemens declared that Sammy must have been behind this prank, and a smart cuffing he deserved.

"Those dogs could have just wandered under that floor," Uncle John pointed out.

Suddenly exasperated and angry, the Judge demanded, "Why is Sammy such a precious rascal that everyone tries to defend him?"

Uncle John chuckled. "Judge, what do you suppose the voice told Moses? You think Aunt Nell will know?"

Judge Clemens thought that blaspheming the Sabbath was enough of an outrage without making a joke of it. "Jane," he said, turning suddenly, "do you think Sammy did this?"

Jane Clemens sighed. "Sammy is like a book that's come alive," she answered vaguely. "If you tear out the pages where he's a rascal, you spoil the best part of the story."

"That tells me nothing, Jane. I suspect he ought to be whipped on general principles."

Sam spent the afternoon in the Quarters with Puss and Uncle Dan'l. By supper the Judge had forgotten that he wanted to cane Sammy. Uncle John's spirits bubbled over until bedtime.

6.

Cross Mr. Cross

AUTUMN WAS one of the best seasons in Hannibal. The sugar and rock maples turned scarlet; across the hills and along the banks of the old river the sumac brightened the day with flashes of crimson; the hickories donned cloaks of burnished gold, and the leaves of the red oaks deepened to purple. Geese honked southward down the valley, and wild pigeons filled the woods. Tom taught Sam a trick he had learned from Bence. At night if fires were lighted to dazzle the pigeons, they could be knocked out of the trees with a club.

"Bence an' my old man don't eat much else this time of the year," Tom said. Sam sighed happily. What could be better than being back on the old easy footing with Tom?

One afternoon they borrowed a skiff and sailed across the river to the Illinois bottoms. Sam never had seen the pecans hang so heavy. Both boys ate greedily, and then Sam gathered the nuts by the handful and dumped them into the boat. Tom watched curiously until Sam had over a bushel.

"You're like a squirrel frettin' over winter comin'," Tom hooted.

"Ma'll like those pecans."

Tom started to answer, then changed his mind. But Sam could read his thoughts. If Tom took pecans home, either

Bence would pelt him with them, or his drunken father might forget to crack the shells and choke to death. Some would say it'd be good riddance if Tom's old man kicked the bucket, but not Sam. Nobody should have to live alone like Injun Joe. Even Bence or old Blankenship was better than having no one to come home to.

"See your Ma's shuttled you off to Cross's school," said Tom, a hint of surliness in his voice. "He won't teach you much."

"Old Cross thinks he's better'n anybody, but he's got a skunk streak."

"He's hog Irish."

Sam laughed.

"He ain't happy unless he's lickin' somebody," Tom grumbled. "I hear he married a woman once who couldn't stand his nasty temper, so she ran off with an Injun, figuring chasin' buffalo wasn't as bad as puttin' up with him!"

To Sam the rumor was entirely credible. "I'm not taking his guff."

"See that you don't," Tom growled, squinting at a duck that flapped over the skiff. "You don't know it, but old Cross is doing you in for fair." He changed the subject abruptly. "I got a secret I learned from Bence who got it down river from a man who told it to him in exchange for a chaw of tobacco."

Sam's spirits soared. "What?"

"It's about the cave."

"Well, don't keep me on needles."

"What good does it do you to know if you've got to spend all day lickin' old Cross's boots? There ain't nothin' you can do about it!"

Sudden misery filled Sam. Compared to Tom, he was more bound in slavery than Uncle Dan'l. In his mind he saw the bluffs that skirted Lover's Leap. Beyond was Cave Hollow.

The steam ferry *Hannibal* made regular pleasure trips there, but the excursionists didn't know the cave the way Sam did. The most they did was to poke their noses a few feet inside the limestone caverns, shiver at the first glimpse of dripping walls, and scoot off. Deeper down in that cave, Sam could have told them, bats winged by your face when you surprised them with the rays of a guttering candle.

The trail to Cave Hollow ran along the willow-hung banks of the Mississippi, turned inland through a wooded dell for half a mile, and ended at the entrance to the cave. A massive iron door hung there, the lock hammered off by a rock. Sam sat up straighter. If there wasn't some mystery in the cave, there wouldn't be any door. He was a fool not to have guessed that much by himself. Now, more than ever, he burned with yearning to learn Tom's secret. "Couldn't we go up afternoons soon as school's out?"

"What's left of the day then?" Tom scoffed. "If you knowed what that man told Bence about the cave, you'd have no mind to get caught over there at night."

"We can go Saturday."

"Well, mebbe. But I ain't tellin' the secret till we find it, an' then you'll know all right!"

Tom's voice was so sinister that Sam twitched with a chill. "Saturday then? You promise?"

"If I don't forget."

Sam steered the skiff through the bottoms. He guessed that he knew Tom as well as anybody. Tom'd be under his window at daybreak Saturday, meowing like an old cat.

"You going to tell Will and Gull?"

"Reckon so."

"Anyone else?"

"If I think they've got the backbone to risk going with us," Tom answered, adding just enough suspense to make

Sam's remaining days of school that week an agony of weari-
some boredom.

Next morning Sam trudged off to his lessons, hating old
Cross with a full heart. With lackluster eyes he saw the schoolhouse standing in a pleasant grove of vines, plum, and hazel.
The grapevine made good swings, Sam conceded gloomily,
but there wasn't much else he could say for the place. The
stern image of old Cross continued to haunt his mind, and
Sam saw the kind of man who sucked on persimmons so that
his mouth would pucker up and he'd be sure never to smile.
Yet his impetuous nature fully enjoyed the period before
the bell rang for school to begin. Then the grove thrummed
with the noise of a dozen games being played at once—fox,
three-cornered cat, catch, hide-'n-whoop.

Sam also liked the new friends he made. Gawky, good-
humored Johnny Briggs joked about everything, even his
father who worked as a stemmer in the tobacco factory.
Jimmy McDaniel's old man kept a candy store, but Jimmy
declared he never touched the stuff. Either Jimmy was a
first-class liar, Sam decided, or his teeth were doing a lot
of rotting away for nothing. Ed Stevens, the jeweler's son,
claimed a distinction almost as unique, for Ed wore clothes
as neat as a pin without being a sissy. He could handle his
fists in a fight. When Ed's earlobes began to burn—a sign, in
Sam's phrase, that an old humpbacked cat was arching up in
Ed—even Tom respected him.

Tom had initiated this trio, as well as Will and Gull,
into the secret plan. Each of them, meeting Sam, spat out
of the corner of his mouth, "Saturday! See you by the willows!" Sam nodded eagerly. Then the school bell rang, and
happy anticipations were buried under the bleak drudgery
of imprisonment.

William O. Cross possessed a skittish Irish temperament
and a nasty temper. If Sam believed that the schoolmaster

thoroughly detested girls and boys—but boys more—little
in the man's sour countenance contradicted that impression.
Cross stood in the doorway, hands on hips and the persimmon-
sucking expression on his mouth, waiting as the children
filed into the room. He watched them cuffing, whispering, pushing, giggling, or punching each other for precisely
ten seconds before his bile overflowed. "Extra sums for
everybody! Extra reading! You've been told over and over.
Gull Brady, you snap that big toe once more, and I'll break
it off. Sam Clemens, put your hands on the desk. There isn't
a fly in this room that needs to be caught. Quiet! Do you hear,
I want it quiet!"

As Cross was now shouting at the top of his lungs while
the sweat poured down his red face, Sam couldn't see how
quiet would be restored until the teacher shut up. The day
opened with a prayer and a hymn. Then the multiplication
class, the reading class, and the grammar class were set to
their parrotlike tasks. Cross stalked the aisles, hands behind
his back, fist pounding palm, a symbol of belligerent authority. He kicked the stove door shut, obviously wishing, in
Sam's opinion, that it was some boy's head. Behind old Cross's
back, Sam scribbled furiously on his slate and passed it to
John Briggs, who snickered violently against the back of
his hand. Sam had written:

> Cross by name and cross by nature—
> Cross jumped over an Irish potato.

Sam's gift as a poet entranced Johnny Briggs. At noon
Cross dismissed the group in a manner indicating that the
sight of them had come close to driving him out of his mind,
and plunged down the hill into town. Inspired by Sam's
couplet, John Briggs lingered and wrote every word on the
blackboard.

When Will Bowen returned from lunch, he was walking on a cloud. For five cents and a jew's harp he had bought a louse. "Fellow said he's an educated one," Will declared. Sam whistled. "Like the fleas in the circus?"

Will nodded, and Sam's eyes sparkled. Since Will and he shared the same desk, they clearly must share the louse.

"What'll you do with him?"

"I'll think of something."

"Cross'll skin you if he finds out."

"Hang Cross! He's not as smart as this louse!"

Meanwhile Cross stomped back to school in a mood that matched his name. He went into the schoolhouse for the bell, and there on the blackboard was Sam's couplet. Word by word, his tight little mouth read noiselessly:

> Cross by name and cross by nature—
> Cross jumped over an Irish potato.

What the man lacked in humor he made up for in a sensitive, thin-skinned vanity. His face flaming, he turned toward the cupboard where he kept his cane. Then, clanging the bell like a warning of thunderous doom, he waited—foot tapping angrily on the floor, cane tapping ominously on the desk. Every giggle, every poke in the ribs as the students filed in and caught sight of the blackboard was another nettle jabbing his temper. At last, his voice went off like the *Jeanie Deans's* gauge cock. "*Who* wrote this?"

A tomblike silence answered him.

"John Briggs!"

"Yes, sir."

Cross strode down the aisle, his cane flicking the edge of each desk like the tongue of a puff adder. The veins in his temples were enlarged and inflamed.

"Stand up, Briggs."

"Yes, sir."

"Is *that* your handwriting?"

Sam fought desperately not to meet John's eyes, which were beseeching him with a numb, doglike pleading to acknowledge his authorship of the couplet. But old Cross hadn't asked who had composed those lines, Sam reasoned, looking away quickly. Even as he did so, he confessed his own cowardice.

"*Is it?*" screamed Cross.

Briggs swallowed hard, abashed by Sam's betrayal. Old Cross's stormy eyes burned through his skull, seeking the truth. "Yes, sir, it is," Briggs admitted defiantly.

The teacher cried out in triumph, and reached for the boy's ear. Step by step he yanked the howling Briggs down the aisle. All over the room boys and girls winced. Ed Stevens doubled up his fists, wishing he were a foot taller so he could pitch into the man, and Gull sucked in his breath with a mournful gasp.

Old Cross used a cane like an artist. He could switch with the right hand or the left, straight down or across the waist. He hit hard, passionate in the belief that he who spared the rod spoiled those children who endured. Sam couldn't hold back a sob, compounded in part of miserable sympathy, in part of horrible guilt. Poor Briggs seemed to bounce with the blows. Tears streamed down his cheeks. Cross dealt him a blow for good measure, glared at the whimpering boy, struck him again and then flung aside the cane.

"Now we'll take up our spelling," he said calmly.

Briggs made his way painfully back to his desk. His angry glance sought Sam. Passing the desk where Sam cowered beside Will, he hissed out the side of his mouth, "You'll get yours, later."

In time the tension eased, principally because Old Cross now seemed in better humor. Will drew the louse from his pocket. He marked two parallel lines about an inch apart down the length of his slate and set the louse between them.

"What'll you bet he crosses my line first?" Will whispered to Sam.

"My pocket knife."

"Against what?"

"The slate and the louse."

"You're on!"

Sam and Will bent over the slate. Both waited tensely. If, as Will claimed, the insect had been educated, then it must have been trained to sit quietly, for it did not move in either direction. Sam blew on it, trying to give it a nudge. Will jiggled the desk. Ear to ear, the boys watched. The louse moved a bit, around and around. Two breaths sucked in above it. At last the louse appeared to understand its task. It began to edge toward Will's line.

"Stop jiggling like that," Sam rasped in hoarse indignation.

"You tried to blow it over to your side."

"I did not!"

Suddenly the louse stopped, as though human voices wearied it. Sam blew harder. Will jiggled the desk with mounting passion. The louse began to move again. Will strained, agonized to see it was moving away from his line. With equal intensity, Sam strained to pull the insect faster across the slate. The louse slipped and skidded.

"Come on, come on!" Sam whispered hoarsely. "Get shoving, you lousy louse!"

"Git—git around," rasped Will. "Devil take you, that's the wrong way!"

Neither boy noticed old Cross approach, craftily on tiptoe. All at once he was there, leaning over their shoulders, watching. Both hands shot out, seizing an ear in each, and he chuckled like a delighted angler who has hooked two catfish at once. Numbers never tired Cross's arms; he chopped

timber during the summer. He caned Will till the boy was
on his knees, howling for mercy. Then he caned Sam, who
danced wildly, but not cleverly enough to throw off the
teacher's aim. Not quite satisfied, he caned the boys in
tandem.

"I can keep this up all day if anyone else would like it,"
Cross announced pleasantly to the forty faces glowering at
him with common malevolence. "Now to get back to our
spelling . . ."

After school John Briggs conceded that, in the end, Sam
had suffered as much as he had. Tom listened in scandalized
sympathy. "Over in the Illinois bottoms," he said, "there's
a morass where you could drown Cross easy. Nobody'd find
him for weeks."

"I wish I knew how to get him there," Sam snarled.

"Mebbe Injun Joe would kill him for a dollar," John
Briggs suggested. Tom thought fifty cents was a fair price.
Jimmy McDaniel nodded wisely and picked at his bad teeth.
The vision was sweet, but the reality remained bitter. Prob-
ably not while it would do them any good was there likely
to be an end to old Cross's tyranny.

7.

Cave Hollow

OLD CROSS could cane his students till their bottoms burned, their legs bled, and his own arms fell off, but the instant Saturday dawned the schoolmaster dropped out of their thoughts the way a dead dog disappears when it is thrown into a bog. Sam awoke, tingling with the prospect of another beautiful autumn day. He rolled over, blinking in the sun and remembering the secret of the cave that Tom had learned from Bence who had heard it firsthand from a man down river in exchange for a chew of tobacco. Any mystery so craftily communicated by word of mouth possessed a ring of truth. Sam bolted from bed and was already dressed when Tom's muffled meow sounded under the window.

By the banks of the Mississippi the two boys breakfasted on wild pigeons that Tom had knocked out of a tree the night before. In the marshes along the river Sam spotted geese, brant, ducks, and cranes. Someone had killed a deer and left the carcass in the willows where the path to Cave Hollow dipped into the woods.

"Injun Joe did that," Tom said. "You can tell by all the blood around. I reckon an Injun figures it's bad manners to kill anything less'n you butcher it on the spot."

"Wouldn't be much left of Injun Joe less he fattened up

on venison when he could," Sam said. "He hibernates like
a bear all through the winter."

Tom roasted the pigeons, turning them on a spit while the
drippings sizzled in the fire. Sam licked his fingers, wishing
the others would show up so they could start for Cave
Hollow.

In his mind he pictured the cave, its dark, gloomy passages leading deep into the earth's silences—even under the
old river, some declared. Those passages opened into majestic
vaulted chambers that had been given names like "The Drawing Room," "The Cathedral," "Aladdin's Palace." Huge stalactites hung from the domes, where bats packed themselves
in bunches and descended in squeaking, darting masses whenever light disturbed them. The cave was a childhood paradise for playing hide-and-seek, but in the summer it was
often filled with excursionists. Sam was glad the steam ferry
stopped running to Cave Hollow this time of year. Some
people in Hannibal still called the place Simms Cave after
the hunter Jack Simms, who had discovered it in 1819. Others
used its second name, Saltpeter Cave; but now most said
McDowell Cave after the doctor in St. Louis who had bought
the property a few years ago.

"You know anything about this doctor, Tom?"

"Only what Bence heard."

"Some say he's touched in the head."

"And mebbe they ain't wrong," Tom said darkly. "I don't
hold with doctors who cut people open 'n' poke around their
insides as though snoopin' for buried treasure."

"Is that the kind of doctor this McDowell is?"

"That and worse. You'll find out." Tom, on the verge of
revealing what Bence had learned from that man down river,
clammed up and glared at the fire.

Sam bristled with a hundred more questions, but now there
were noises in the willows, and Ed Stevens appeared with

John Briggs and Jimmy McDaniel. Will and Gull arrived moments later. Tom took command—a natural prerogative, since he knew the secret.

"You know that third room in the cave—the one called Aladdin's Palace, about as far in as anyone ever goes?" he asked. "Off to the left of that room, there's another passage going deeper into the earth."

"I've been down there," Ed complained. "There's nothing much in there."

"Shut up till I finish, you dash know-it-all. Because you *don't* know. And crazy old McDowell doesn't *want* you to know. But if you go round those things hangin' down from the ceiling on t'other side, 'n' clean away the rock 'n' dirt piled there, 'n' get down on your hands 'n' knees, you'll find another openin' that goes down 'n' down 'n' down!"

Ed's quizzical eyes said seeing would be believing, but Jimmy McDaniel whistled, and Gull gave his toe a quick, excited snap. Sam blurted out the query that entranced them all. "What's down there, Tom?"

"More'n you expect."

"Is—is it dangerous?"

"You'll see!"

"Waitin' and blabbin' don't pick no cotton," Will growled impatiently. "Let's go look for ourselves."

The group raced through the woody hollow, and the half mile to the cave melted behind them. Tom pushed open the door. Daylight penetrated the passage for only a short distance, then darkness and silence confronted them.

"Take care to keep your candles lit," Tom warned. "I ain't hankering to get caught down there—not even as far as Aladdin's Palace—without a light."

All at once Jimmy didn't possess much hankering to go anywhere. The boy stood, miserably undecided, his backbone turning as soft as his teeth.

"Pigeon feet had better stop right here," Tom growled ominously.

Jimmy looked even more miserable. "Jimmy'll stick with me," said Sam. "He'll be all right."

"If you lose him, an' he dies down there, don't blame me," Tom flung back. He had produced the effect he wanted, for Jimmy swallowed his candy in one gulp, and his teeth began to chatter.

Sam threw the frightened boy a quick smile. Only once had his sympathy for an underdog failed him—the day he watched John Briggs take a caning for the couplet he had written. The shame of that cowardice had troubled Sam for two nights. He wasn't ever going to be that chicken-livered again. "Pay no heed to Tom," Sam said. "He's just being a big mouth."

The passages to Aladdin's Palace were reasonably familiar to everyone, and the boys joked and pushed each other as they tramped through them. But in Aladdin's Palace, the stalactites over their heads hung eerily, and the walls oozed with moisture. The warm air was more close and felt heavier in their lungs. The candles flickered under drafts a person couldn't feel; yet they were there, a part of a world that existed in darkness. The boys fell into a silence that grew and deepened and circled around behind them, until they, too, seemed to become part of the eternal silence of this subterranean domain.

Tom moved cautiously to the place where the hidden passage should be. He and Ed Stevens raked away a pile of rock and dirt that looked freshly made. Suddenly Tom sucked in his breath. For once in his life, Bence was telling the truth. There *was* another opening! Sam and Jimmy, John Briggs, Will and Gull gathered around the entrance, gaping nervously into the mysterious darkness. Johnny Briggs declared that he heard rushing water down there.

"Mebbe we'll be beneath the Mississippi if we go down," Jimmy McDaniel muttered worriedly. "Mebbe that old river'll pour in all at once and trap us!"

"Oh, catfish and kittens!" Gull exploded. "If you hear anything, it's a little underground stream, that's all."

"I bet there's a million bats in there," Will grumbled.

Ed asked the practical question. "Who's going first?"

And Sam gave the practical answer. "Tom, you've led this far. You go."

"I ain't afraid."

"Then go."

"You goin' to follow?"

"You want me to go first?"

In the flickering candlelight Tom glared at Sam. Then, cupping his hand carefully around the guttering flame of his candle, he climbed through the opening. He went only a few yards before he stopped, making certain that the others had followed.

Will had underestimated the bat population, for suddenly the air was filled with a hissing and a squeaking and a whirring and a whooshing. The passage was alive with bats darting past, and the boys knocked them away from their faces and the candles. There must have been two million bats, Sam thought, before the menace was behind them. Then Jimmy McDaniel stopped short and howled piteously. His candle had gone out. Sam relighted it from his own, but the feat proved difficult; Jimmy's hand was shaking as though he had palsy.

With Jimmy quieted, Tom went ahead, carefully testing each step. Sam, next in line, could hear his thick breathing and feel his hot breath whenever Tom turned his head.

"Where did Bence say this passage leads, Tom?"

"Into another room like the one we just left."

"What's in there?"

Tom sloshed through a tiny stream of water that trickled ankle-deep across the floor of the passageway before he answered. "The man told Bence there'd be cannon and mebbe 500 stand of small arms."

"What would they be doing here?"

"That crazy doctor put 'em there."

"But why, Tom? There'd have to be some reason."

"The fool's got some wild idea 'bout organizin' his own army an' invadin' Mexico."

"No!"

"That's what the man said, an' Bence ain't got the brains to dream up an idea like that."

"But how did this man know, Tom?"

"He used to work for the doctor. Once, he said, he had to cart away the corpse of some fellow McDowell had cut up, and that was the end for him."

A chill arched Sam's back till he felt like a tomcat. He kept close to Tom, letting Jimmy McDaniel worry for himself, although he knew by the click-click-clicking of the other boy's teeth that he was never very far behind.

"Did the man help to put the cannon and guns down here, Tom?"

"That's what he said. Also the *other* thing."

Sam's heart skipped a beat. Tom was speaking as though his mouth was full of fears of all sizes. "What—what other thing, Tom?" Sam insisted.

But Tom wasn't play-acting this time. He was dead serious when he answered. "Sam, even I've got to see *that* to believe it!"

The passage was wider now, and soon they entered another chamber. This was the worst part, thought Sam; now
there wasn't any decent, self-respecting way to turn back
without encountering *it*—whatever it was!

At first, as their eyes grew accustomed to the dim shapes
and images in the expanse before them, they saw only the
strangely beautiful pillars formed by the joining of stalactites
and stalagmites. Water dripping for centuries had shaped
these underground marvels, and for a time no one uttered
a word as the wonder of their surroundings caught at their
throats and rendered them speechless. Sam started counting
the columns nature had made, but there were dozens of them,
each about as big as a man's leg. Ed Stevens discovered the
basin of a spring by almost falling into it; the glittering crys-
tals incrusted around its edge looked like frosty patterns on
a windowpane after a cold winter night.

"You see those guns?" Sam whispered to Tom.

"My eyes ain't got used to catching shapes right yet. This
is a mighty big room, an' I guess you could hide a good part
of Hannibal in here."

Off to their left, Gull raised a startled squawk. "Hey!
There's a cannon over here!"

Across the wavering candlelight Tom's glance met Sam's.
Then the down-river man hadn't been hoodwinking Bence!

An investigation revealed two more cannon—blunt-nosed
six-pounders that could knock down a stone wall at close
range—and piles of crates containing small arms. Will and
John Briggs searched for kegs of gunpowder and shot but
couldn't find either—a good thing, Jimmy McDaniel declared through his jingling teeth, for some fool might drop
a lighted candle and blow them all to kingdom come.

Tom explained the incredible story to the others. "What's
he got against Mexicans?" Will asked.

"Nothin' more'n Pawnees has against Osages, I guess," Tom said. "The sight of one makes the other sick."

"Would you go fight, Tom, if you got the chance, and they gave you a gun?"

"With that crazy doctor? I reckon not!"

"Americans could whip those lazy Mexicans if they had a mind to," Gull said.

"Mebbe they could," John Briggs declared, "but you ain't going to feel any less dead with a Mexican bullet in your belly."

Sam, as curious as Gull or Will, poked around the cannon and crates, but always lurking at the back of his mind was what Tom had said about the *other* thing. "Where is it, Tom?"

"The man told Bence it was in a copper cylinder."

"Do you see one?"

"I . . . I ain't really looked." Nor did he have much heart to, Tom's tone added.

Sam swung the candle around his head, squinted, then drew in his breath sharply. "Over by that pillar there, Tom. Look!"

Tom squinted in the direction Sam's finger pointed. "Reckon that's it."

"It looks awful big."

"Guess mebbe it has to be."

Sam didn't like the way Tom's manner was giving him the shivers. "What did Bence say was in that cylinder?"

"You can look if you want to."

"All right, I will!"

But Sam's knees were wobbling as he advanced toward the copper cylinder, and his hand holding the candle trembled. As if hypnotized, Tom followed Sam's candle. The two boys stared down at the huge barrel.

"It's got a cover, but it'll come off easy. You can see it's loose."

Sam slid off the lid. A liquid filled the cylinder almost to the brim. "Smells like alcohol, Tom."

"That's what it is."

"Well, what's so bad about that?"

Tom nodded toward a long stick that leaned against a pillar. "Stir it up with that."

Sam hesitated, catching Tom's jumpiness as though it was a communicable disease, like measles or cholera. Then he handed his candle to Tom.

"Hold this for me."

Sam took the stick and plunged it into the cylinder. It struck something solid and heavy, and for a moment the surprise paralyzed him.

"Give her a stir," Tom said hoarsely. "We *gotta* see now."

Sam stirred, using all his strength. Slowly the object in the cylinder began to move. Suddenly, Tom let out a horrified yelp. Sam, too, gave a yell filled with terror. "Y-y-you see it, Tom?"

"It was a f-f-face—a young g-g-girl's face!"

"Tom, she's dead!"

"You can't stay alive pickled in alcohol."

"Tom, let's get outta here! Let the others hang around and stare if they want. Let's get all the way out—clear back to Hannibal!"

"Come on!" Tom said, scrambling off.

Years had to pass before Sam learned that eccentric Dr. E. D. McDowell wasn't crazy, as Tom claimed. Orion could have told him that Dr. McDowell was a respected resident of St. Louis, who ran his own medical school. Of course, even Orion could not know that there was no need for the doctor to organize and equip a private army; within a few years, the whole country would be at war with Mexico. As for the cadaver in the cylinder, Sam and Tom knew only what the man told Bence. The body was that of a fourteen-year-old girl—some said later she was McDowell's own daughter, who had died—and the doctor was experimenting to see if the limestone caverns would petrify her. Once the secret of the cave was known, the cannon and guns were removed, but the copper cylinder remained there for years. Sam claimed that excursionists of "the baser order" would stir up the alcohol and stare at the face. He never went back himself.

For weeks after Sam learned the secret of Cave Hollow he tossed at night. He even returned to a habit that had troubled him when he was Henry's age. When Sam walked the hall with arms outstretched, Henry would set up a howl for Ma, and she'd nudge the Judge. Together, they'd turn the sleepwalking Sam back toward his bed.

After a time winter arrived, cold as the arctic, freezing the old Mississippi and turning the hill by old Cross's school into a whiz for sleighing. Time helped dim the image of the dead girl's face, even in Sam Clemens' overactive imagination.

8.

Sam Can't Wait

ALONG THE MISSOURI border in the 1840's people didn't sniff when a child managed to live for nine years. A great many didn't make it. With Sam—and Henry had been right when he had quoted Ma as saying Sammy had been a puny baby—the struggle between life and death had often been touch and go. No one knew better than Jane Clemens how fierce the fight had been. For the first seven years Sam had seemed glued together by the sticky medicines poured down his wailing throat. He believed that Ma bought castor oil a barrel at a time.

Sammy sick or Sammy well was pretty much the same problem to Jane Clemens. There was no sense thinking he could be like any other sensible sick child. Sam wasn't quite five when the medical profession, in as far as it touched Hannibal, was mystified by a new and terrifying addition to the already horrendous list of frontier illnesses.

Pamela ran into the kitchen, tears streaming down her face. "Ma, Sammy's dying! Ma, Sammy's dying!"

Jane Clemens fled upstairs to find Sam squirming and gagging in convulsions. "Go for Dr. Meredith," she told Pamela. "And don't go bawling through the street either, for that won't save Sammy."

Then Jane Clemens looked down at her son. It was hard to believe, but her eyes were good, and the boy's mouth was full of worms. Jane Clemens knew how to treat worms. She dosed Sammy good with salt as a vermifuge. Weak and gasping, the boy had started to recover from his convulsions by the time a still-screaming Pamela ushered in Dr. Meredith to watch Sammy die.

An old ex-sailor with a gruff bass voice that could reach a river steamer a quarter of a mile from port, Hugh Meredith exploded. "Worms! Where in tarnation would he get worms?"

"Look there," Jane Clemens said with spirit. "They were in his mouth."

"Did he put 'em there himself?"

"Why would he do anything so ridiculous?"

"Salt! Pouring salt down a child like that! You wouldn't treat a horse that way."

"What was I to do? Let the child choke to death?"

Dr. Meredith wouldn't say. Sam's convulsions and worms were a mystery to him. "For the love of Jupiter, call me if this happens again and let me do the doctoring!"

Sam spent the remainder of the day in bed. Pamela fussed over him, Pa came in and gazed down benevolently as though thankful he were still alive, and Ma brought him supper. Having convulsions had worked out fine. But Sam never again possessed the courage to stuff live worms in his mouth. Anyhow, Ma was crafty. The same trick wouldn't fool her twice.

Yet in large measure Sam's numerous illnesses were nature's invention and not his own. He grew to regard Dr. Meredith with sour thoughts, wishing the man had never given up the sea. "You can't look into my mouth without slopping me with castor oil," Sam wailed.

"I can't look into your mouth without expecting to see

a new batch of worms. Thus far the oil's drowned them."

Sometimes for variety Dr. Meredith dosed Sam with calomel, rhubarb, and jalap.

Judge Clemens was as bad, if not worse. Along with his knowledge of the law, Sam's father believed himself to be an authority on home remedies. Socks full of hot ashes, poultices and purges, blue-mass pills—Sam was exposed to all of Pa's pet treatments.

"You're still alive," the Judge said, impervious to Sam's howls.

"Only part of me's alive," Sam grumbled. "I feel as though that part's already dying."

But the Judge couldn't be moved, nor could Jane Clemens. Sam's parents had seen three of their children die—a daughter Margaret and two sons, Pleasants and Benjamin—and for all that Sammy was a terror, they intended to hold on to him.

So no matter how wild Sam wanted to run, Jane Clemens was glad that he was there to run at all. The fear never entirely faded that at any moment an epidemic might steal up the river, claiming its victims by the dozens. The spring of 1843 had brought a cholera scare, which happily passed without calamity except for the painkiller youngsters were forced to drink and which Sam, in a spirit of Christian brotherhood, forced on the cats, transforming the Clemens kitchen into rather a mean-tempered place. Then another spring pushed up the valley, scenting the air with the fragrance of locust trees, brightening the hills with the blooms of dogwood and redbud, and starting the jimson weed that by dry August would choke out most of the grass in Hannibal yards. And 1844 brought another epidemic—one that kept the dead-wagon rolling cheerlessly and almost constantly down the hill and out the winding country road to the burial ground.

Sam spent a week cooped up in the house—at war with Henry, Pamela, and Ma.

"Indeed you're not going out," Jane Clemens stormed, repeating once more the words she had said so often. "You're not taking one step through that door till these measles pass!"

"Everybody makes a fuss over little things!"

Ma's eyes flashed. "Seven dead in one day! You think that isn't worth a fuss?"

"I didn't play with any of them."

Sam goaded Jane Clemens into telling him something she had intended not to mention. "Your friend, Will Bowen, is in bed right now running a fever that's made him half-delirious."

Shock filled Sam's eyes. "Ma, is Will going to die?"

"Nobody knows what the Lord will decide," Jane Clemens said in a gentler voice. "Dr. Meredith is doing the best he can."

"That old harpooner! All he knows is tearing your insides out with castor oil—barrels of it, not just kegs. If the measles don't kill Will, then old Meredith's bound to finish him with that stuff."

Ma, on the point of a sharp reply, bit her tongue. She could see how deeply Sam had been affected by the news about Will. "We must all hope for poor Will, Sammy. And pray—we must all pray hard."

Nothing in Sam's constitution permitted him to sit all day and pray. Memories of the good times he had known with Will crowded his thoughts. He saw Will swimming in Bear Creek, and play-acting King Arthur's Court in the wooded seclusion of Holliday's Hill, and racing that louse on the slate and taking the caning from old man Cross. He saw Will's enormous, shining eyes in the cave when they had found the guns and copper cylinder, and Will perched in the apple tree splitting his sides with laughter when the cats took over the Western Star Tavern, and Will's bare feet kicking up dust across Wildcat Corner when John Hannick's roaring "Steeammm-*boat* a-comin'!" set the whole town of Hannibal in motion.

"Will's my best friend," Sam decided, and into his stomach and up through his chest rose an awful hollow feeling. How empty Hannibal would seem if Will were to die!

At the sound of Judge Clemens entering the house, Sam fled down the stairs. "Pa, is Will any better? Pa, did you hear anything?"

Sadly the Judge answered, "There hasn't been any change, Sammy. Will's still a very sick boy."

Sam didn't want supper, but Ma forced him to eat, saying he must keep his health and strength so that he wouldn't get the measles. Sam went up to bed afterward, worried, filled with gloomy forebodings, and bored sick with the captivity that now had lasted for over a week and would still go on for days and days. "Anything's better than this," he muttered unhappily. "Even having the measles—and dying."

That night, stretched out in bed with his hands under his head and his eyes gazing through the window at the myriad of stars, the boy turned over in his mind a new and tantalizing reflection. What was so bad with dying? First you got sick, and people paid attention to you, and you weren't cooped up all alone moping from one day to the next. Everybody in the family gathered around you and cried their hearts out and swore they always had loved you no matter what you had done, and you felt pretty good, except that there had been some things you had been afraid to do which you could see now you might as well have done since everybody was going to bawl just as hard anyhow.

"Will's the lucky one," Sammy grumbled. "What happens to him *counts*."

Sam's imagination resumed its pleasant reverie. He saw Ma standing by the bed with her eyes melting with love, and Pamela in a flood of tears, and Pa standing there and begging Sammy to forgive him for selling Jennie down the river and for riding off to the farm without him, and Henry saying something sassy, and Ma boxing his ears, and Pa yanking him out to the woodshed and beating him to within an inch of his life . . . on the end of a long sigh Sam murmured, "It's a great thing to die." Of course Ma would write to Aunt Patsy and Uncle John, and they would just sit praying before the fireplace all day, and Puss would go right down to the tobacco house and dive into the forbidden swimming hole and maybe drown herself in his memory, and Aunt Nell would be so mad at Uncle Dan'l because Sammy was dying that she would strike him mute with lockjaw, and all over the Quarters the Negroes would be moaning and singing spirituals and petting those hound dogs for giving dear little Sammy so much fun by chasing the hogs under the church floor.

Sam sensed the wonderful moment of climax. He would catch a glimpse of Orion, rushing in breathless after killing eight horses in his all-night ride from St. Louis. Sam would smile and forgive everybody in the family, even that stinker Henry. He would watch Orion working his jaws, getting ready to deliver a lecture on how nobody should pass through the Valley of the Shadow without washing his hands and face, and then Sam would do what he always had wanted to do in such moments—he would drop dead. His cloud and his harp would be waiting, and he would ride up to heaven, barefooted.

Sleep closed Sam's eyes on a beautiful smile as though, indeed, his last breath had just been drawn. But the sun came up presently, rousing Sam into blinking wakefulness and back to another endless day of nothing to do. He felt like crying at the realization of his desperate loneliness.

Anything—just dash-dang anything—would be better, his

constricted spirit told him. Right there Sam reached a decision. He sprang out of bed and into his clothes.

"Dead or alive," he muttered, "I'm going to get it over with." And Sam slipped through the window, slid across the shed roof, and dropped noiselessly to the ground.

Only the chickens seemed to be awake in Hannibal. Quick strides carried Sam down the hill to Will Bowen's house. Here, too, the world appeared to be wrapped in slumber. Sam couldn't have asked for better luck. Now if the Bowens had left the kitchen door unlatched as they usually did, his cup of joy would overflow.

Fortune continued to smile brightly on Sam—the door was unlatched. He tiptoed across the kitchen and up the stairs to Will's room. Within, Will tossed in bed, moaning slightly, his half-conscious mind tormented by days of high fever. Sam entered the chamber, closed the door, and took off his clothes. Then he crawled into bed beside Will and pulled up the covers. "I'll get 'em, and now there'll be a finish to it, one way or the other," Sam murmured triumphantly.

Sam didn't do the job halfway. By the time Mrs. Bowen discovered him in bed with Will and shrieked for Mr. Bowen, who then wrapped him in a blanket and carried him home, Sam had caught germs enough to develop a case of measles that Dr. Meredith pronounced among the worst in Hannibal.

"Young fool deserves to die," the ex-sailor said gruffly.

"Please don't say that," Jane Clemens cried, stricken at the thought.

"Can't anybody teach him some sense?"

"I won't have you abuse Sammy," Jane Clemens said sharply. "Not when he may be at death's door."

Dr. Meredith harrumphed into his mustache, pretty mad at Sam. He was overworked and felt as though he were halfway through death's door himself. He ached all over and wondered why he didn't go back to sailing.

"His fever'll get worse," the doctor said grumpily.

Judge Clemens entered the bedroom, his face strained with worry. "How much higher will it go?" Pa asked.

Hugh Meredith threw up his hands. "How do I know? Sam gets worms at the wrong end—how can you tell? He may boil over like a tea kettle."

Pamela stood in the doorway, immersed in a virtual flood of tears as Sam had expected, and Henry peeked around her, obviously calculating if he could have Sammy's books when he died. The sick boy closed his eyes, contented. Had Orion been sent for? Had Ma written Aunt Patsy and Uncle John, and had Aunt Nell, outraged that this should happen to Sammy, struck down Uncle Dan'l with lockjaw? Everything was working out fine.

But then fortune deserted Sammy. His fever went up and stayed up. For days he was a rolling, tossing, delirious lump in the bed. He didn't know Ma was in the room, or how often Dr. Meredith called, or how red grew Pamela's poor swollen eyes. Days came, days went, and for Sam the period was like a hole punched in his life. By the time the crisis had passed, and he was aware once more of his surroundings, the edge of his triumph had worn pretty thin.

Yet there was still a chance he would die, Sam thought. There was still hope. Ma had come into the room a few minutes ago, and Sam decided that he would be sweet to Ma and let her see he wasn't afraid to die—not one bit. Sam rolled over, filled with pleasant anticipations, and made a dreadful discovery that was like a slap in the face. Jane Clemens sat in a rocker, sound asleep!

A rush of anger consumed Sam. "Ma! Ma!" he shouted as loudly as he could.

Wearily the woman lifted her head and asked in a wooden, careworn voice, "Yes, Sammy?"

"Ma, what's the sense of dying if you're going to sleep right through it?"

"That wouldn't be much fun at all, would it, Sammy?"

"I'm not dying that way!" Sam exclaimed hotly.

Even with the tiredness of nursing him through the hard days about which he would never know, Jane Clemens still possessed the reserve for a quick and tender smile.

"No, Sammy," she said, "you're not going to die. Like the rest of us, you're cursed with putting up with the worst villain ever created—life itself. So you'll just have to go on, letting your good side fight the bad, while the villain tries to beat you down and make you his slave. If he wins with you, Sammy, I give up. You were born to outwit the devil!"

And Jane Clemens arose, and pulled the covers around Sam, and touched his head gently. Then she went heavily down the stairs to her supper, leaving the boy to mull over this thought for the rest of his life.

9.

Bence

AT TEN, SAM was a leggy, loose-jointed lad whose bush of sandy hair was still vigorously licked flat across his head and around his ears. His eyes, once an opalescent green in bright sunlight, like the eyes of a cat, now turned grayish. In the two years since Sam had crawled into bed beside the semi-delirious Will Bowen, determined that he would have the measles without fear of the consequences, he had grown steadily in health and strength. Even Sam now conceded that it was a good thing he hadn't been too hasty in claiming his cloud and harp and riding off to heaven, barefooted. And, if it was true, as Ma said, that he was born to outwit the devil, the race between Sam and Satan was still going full tilt. Poor Ma, if she had time to ponder the matter, must have wondered seriously whether Sam's good side would ever gain on the clown and mischief-maker.

But Jane Clemens had other worries that summer of 1846; rather, she rubbed elbows harder with *the* worry. Sam often overheard Ma and Pa talking in the kitchen until long after most folk in Hannibal were sound asleep.

"I guess we're forced to it at last," the Judge said gloomily. "There's no recourse but to sell the Tennessee land."

Jane Clemens drummed her fingers on the table with such

heavy thoughtfulness that Sam, propped up in bed, could hear her. Then Ma asked, "Do you really think that land will some day make the children well-to-do?"

"If we can wait to sell it till we can get a fair price, Jane, it'll be a bonanza."

"John, you're such a dreamer. All your life you've been living bottled up in this dream. It's been your reason for getting up in the morning and working all day and going to bed at night."

"I know I'm right about that Tennessee land," the Judge said stoically.

"Not that I think it's wrong to live in dreams," Jane Clemens continued as though she hadn't heard. "Orion has a touch of that trait, and at times Sammy doesn't seem to be much more than a bundle of romantic fancies. None of you can run a store—that's too practical. Orion wants to be a lawyer and starve to death. Sammy would probably like to rob stagecoaches. Yet, I'm glad they're your sons. I hope your sense of honor and honesty and decency is planted as deep in them as they are in you."

Ma's speech surprised Sam. He had never felt that he was one bit like Pa; now Ma said that he was, and for the last reason on earth he ever would have suspected. Funny, too, that Ma wouldn't say right out what was clear as crystal between the lines, that if the Judge had been less of a dreamer maybe the Clemenses wouldn't be struggling so hard to hold skin and bone together. But Ma didn't speak bitterly. She didn't scold. She didn't say that she wanted things any different. She was almost tender toward Pa, revealing an affection that no one ever saw on the surface. Sam had seen Ma kiss Pa only once, and that was years ago when his brother Benjamin had died. They weren't smoochers by nature, and yet, Sam could see, deep down inside them—in heart and in spirit—they stuck by one another.

"No, we'll hold on to our dream, for maybe you're right, and it'll all come true. We owe it to the children," Jane Clemens said stoutly. "We'll manage to scrape along some other way."

"I'm not a man who can take a shovel and work in the roads."

"We'll pull through somehow. If the Blankenships can hold on by their toenails, so can we."

Quickly the Judge recaptured his cool, aloof dignity. "Really, Jane, you needn't drag us down that low."

"I mean," Ma said, "that people who want to hang on, do. No more and no less, so don't go picking a quarrel with me."

Sam grinned. Suddenly Ma and Pa sounded more normal. Nature never had intended them for lovebirds, and they did well not to try to be. But before Sam blinked off to sleep that night, hearing the summer noises that filled slumbering Hannibal—the katydids chirping in the jimson weed, the whippoorwills down by the old river, a couple of dogs that were growling nastily and working up to waste a good fight with no one around to see them—his mind lingered on what a fine thing it would be for Ma, and for Pa, too, if the Clemenses could stumble unexpectedly upon a little ready cash. Say fifty dollars. Sam hadn't picked the figure out of the night by whim. An advertisement in the local newspaper offered that amount for the apprehension of a runaway slave.

Next morning Tom suggested that they go to Stringtown, a run-down section west of Hannibal where cabins and stock pens stretched along the road in a straight line. Even here summer had worked a kind of magic. Blackberry bushes and hazel vines filled the angles of the rail fences. The blooming wild flowers smelled sweet.

"Why did you bring me way out here?" Sam asked.

"I wanna find Bence."

"What for? Did you forget to club him over the head?"

"Bence ain't so bad," Tom said, defending him for the first time that Sam could remember. "Not underneath."

"Bence has got to show me."

"Maybe he will."

Sam glanced at Tom and, remembering the copper cylinder in Cave Hollow, began to feel uneasy. "Well, tell me the truth," he said finally. "Has Bence got another confounded secret?"

Tom nodded.

"Here in Stringtown?"

"No. Across the river. Over in the Illinois bottoms."

"Did Bence kill someone?"

"I reckon you've got something to learn about Bence. He ain't Injun Joe. If Bence was, I reckon there wouldn't be nothin' at all over in those bottoms."

Sam put his foot down. "I'm not going through another of Bence's secrets unless I know right now. You say the mystery is over in the bottoms, yet we're looking for Bence in Stringtown. That makes about as much sense as looking under a pond lily for turkey eggs!"

Tom scrutinized Sam sharply, making up his mind whether to tell him anything. "You give me your word an' hope Bence burns your eyes out with a candle if you ever tell?"

"All right. I swear it."

"Well, Bence would. An' maybe I'd help him. Bence an' me's the only ones who know. We'd drown Pap before we'd ever tell him, or at least push him in the river an' let him drown himself." Then Tom drew a deep breath, kicked at a stone, and asked Sam, "You read about the runaway slave?"

"The one they're offering the fifty dollars for?"

"Bence found him—hiding over in the Illinois bottoms!"

Sam whistled. That lucky Bence! When he got the reward, he'd have more ready cash than all the Blankenships likely had seen in the last five years. "What's Bence doing over here in Stringtown then?" he asked.

"They're butchering at the pork houses. Spareribs, livers, parts nobody'll buy they give away free. They're still good eatin'."

Sam could see Bence's plan clear enough. That runaway Negro must be half starved by now; from what Sam remembered of the advertisement, he'd been gone from the plantation for two weeks. So Bence would offer him food, gain his confidence, then jump him and capture him. Somehow Sam didn't like to think of trapping a man because he was so hungry he couldn't protect himself properly. And that slave wasn't any fool. He had made for the Illinois bottoms, where the bloodhounds would quickly lose his scent. Maybe he had rubbed his body with onion to make tracking him even harder for the dogs. Of course, the law said it was every citizen's duty to capture a runaway Negro and return him to his rightful owner, and the law didn't care how it was done. Sam, turning the whole thing over in his mind, admitted that Bence was acting properly. He still wished that there was another way.

"Tom, when does Bence figure on capturing this slave?"

"Huh?" Tom asked, looking up. "Bence ain't figurin' on capturin' that slave at all. Bence's helpin' him hide till he can make a clean getaway."

Sam didn't believe a word Tom said. Tom was just being crafty, throwing Sam off the trail, so he wouldn't come sniveling around for any part of the reward. Sam guessed he knew how much fifty dollars would mean to his own family. Multiply that figure by ten, and you'd have some idea of what the same amount would mean to the Blankenships. More, Sam knew what they did to abolitionists and other property stealers who helped slaves escape. A rope and a tree made a neat package out of such shenanigans. But Sam bit his lip and didn't say anything.

Bence swung down the road toward them. Under his arm were two large parcels of free meat he had gleaned from the pork houses. At the sight of Sam, he turned on Tom and swore loudly and profanely. "I told you not to bring no one!"

"Sam's all right."

"How do you know? Ain't his old man a judge? Him an' the law are thicker'n thieves!"

Even when Bence was relaxed, he was not a pretty sight. In anger, his dark eyes narrowed and turned murky, his full lips curled, his long, flat nostrils twitched, and his ham-sized hands clenched and unclenched as though wishing they could find a neck to wring. Now, savagely, Bence turned on Sam. "You know what I'll do if you blabber?"

"Come off your perch with me, Bence," Sam said, his temper rising at the threat. "I gave Tom my promise. I'll keep it. Anyhow, I'm not looking for any part of the reward."

"See that you don't," Bence said, backing down. Sam smiled to himself. How shrewd he'd been to guess what Bence was after and to disarm him by disclaiming any part of it.

"I know where we can get a skiff that'll take the three of us in comfort over to the bottoms," said Tom.

"Let's get shovin'," Bence retorted. Then, glowering, he said to Sam, "As long as you're comin', you can lug some of this stuff."

Within minutes Bence and the two boys were skimming the waves, for as soon as they rounded the point the long river valley gave the wind a full sweep. Sam breathed deeply. He was back on the river he loved, flashing along between her clean, forested shores, feeling the pull of a tide as strong as anything on earth. Overhead, the sky was so clear that its blueness made even the cloud puffs translucent. He inhaled the smell of the water and tried to sort out the odors of marsh and mud and catfish and drifting timber and the dozen others that somehow blended into this one deep, rich scent. Some called the Mississippi "the great sewer," and maybe the old river did lose her loveliness in places like Memphis and St. Louis where they dumped her full of garbage. But at Hannibal, the Mississippi was at her best, one of nature's beauties that sunlight decked in diamonds and the moon swathed in silver.

They had almost reached the Illinois bottoms before Bence spoke. "This fellow is called Jim."

Sam nodded. "How big is he, Bence?"

"Mebbe seven feet. Mebbe taller. If he had a mind to, he could take you in his hands an' snap you in two."

Tom was handling the tiller as they entered the bottoms, but then Bence took over. Soon Sam realized that they were deeper into the marshes than he and Tom had ever penetrated. Without Bence, they might not find their way out in a week. Presently they came to an island, although Sam reckoned that three or four feet of water probably covered this land when the river flooded. Bence ran the skiff up close and dropped anchor.

They waited a spell, for Bence said that you couldn't always tell whether you had been followed by someone hugging the overhanging foliage along the shore. All you could do was sit and see if they came up and gave themselves away. Half an hour or more elapsed, and Sam realized that this watchful patience was a side of Bence that he wouldn't have guessed. Finally, even Bence appeared satisfied. He puckered up his lips and whistled one 'long and one short trill. He repeated this signal three times before the tall grass parted, and Sam found himself looking into the face of Jim, the runaway slave.

"I got the meat like I promised," Bence called.

"Well, thanks fo' dat." Jim stepped forward, and Sam
saw that Bence hadn't lied. Jim could have been seven feet
tall!

"You still got firewood, Jim?" Bence asked.

"It's runnin' mighty low."

"Too risky, comin' over twice by daylight. I'll bring you
some more tonight."

"Ah kin eat de meat raw."

"Not pork in hot weather. It ain't good for you. Makes
you sick an' sleepy, an' they might catch you then. You wait
till tonight."

"If Ah knows 'bout when you's comin', you won't have
to whistle. Ah'll be here."

"About an hour after sundown," Bence said, nodding.
"Bring you 'taters, too. Didn't have time to let old Selmes
add his bit to your comfort this morning." And Bence
laughed.

Jim turned and vanished in the tall grass. Bence hauled
up the anchor, and soon they were retracing the way through
the bottoms.

"Can me an' Sam come tonight?" Tom begged.

"Specially if I call on Mr. Selmes for his contribution?"
Sam asked.

"Don't make me wait." Bence grumbled. " 'Cause I won't."

Not until they had cleared the bottoms did Sam find the
courage to ask the question that was on his mind. "Bence,
have you thought what you could do with fifty dollars?"

"Me, I could get to New Orleans an' have me a time."

"If Pap didn't find out first," Tom said. "Then you'd both
likker up for a month."

"Well, Pap won't find out 'cause there ain't goin' to be
fifty dollars to swill away."

"You're not turning Jim in?" Sam asked. "Not ever?"

"I guess not!"

"You know what the law says."

"The slaveowners writ the laws, not the slaves."

"Yes, but . . ."

"There ain't no buts," Bence interrupted peevishly. "Law favors those who make 'em. That's the kind of laws never should be writ."

"Don't you want to go to New Orleans?"

"I've thought about it."

"You could now."

"By havin' Jim catched an' sent back? Would you like to be catched that way?"

Sam shook his head unbelievingly. As Tom had said, he had something to learn about Bence—the town bully on the surface, maybe its noblest citizen underneath. Sam fell silent, and Tom took the tiller and steered the skiff to the spot from which they had taken it. Nobody would ever be the wiser.

"See you here tonight, Bence," Sam said.

The older youth climbed out, grunted grumpily, then strode off without answering or looking back.

"He mad at me, Tom?"

"Naw. Bence's thinkin'. It always fries out Bence an' Pap to think."

Swiping the potatoes from Selmes's store was no task with an accomplice of Tom's practiced talents. Sam said they were like Robin Hood and Friar Tuck, robbing the rich to feed the poor. They walked back to Wildcat Corner, happy with their loot, and then they saw something that chilled Sam's blood and made Tom swear.

In slavery country, and especially along the middle border where slave territory joined free state, the professional slave chaser with his dogs and guns, his whip and chains was a common sight. Fat rewards were offered for runaway Negroes, and Sam had seen slave chasers lots of times, lounging around the saloons and the dock, listening to gossip, and making inquiries that might lead them to their quarry. Sam had never paid them much heed; they were a part of Hannibal that meant nothing to him. Now they meant the difference between capture and freedom for Jim!

"Lookit, Tom, the mean way they stand by that store door, listenin'."

"They're mean-livin'!"

"When one man chases down another for profit, it seems low."

"Lower'n river mud."

"I wouldn't mix with 'em—them or slave traders."

"Spit in their faces an' run away, that's how I've a mind to do."

But Sam was irresistibly attracted to the slave chasers. One was lean, and one was fat. Mr. Bones wore a beard, and Mr. Belly was clean-shaven. One smoked a cigar, and the other chewed tobacco. Outwardly they looked quiet and respectable, and, of course, the law was on their side. Sam didn't doubt for a moment that Pa would speak to them and try to help them.

Tom was skittish in their presence. "Come on, let's shed the sight of those mud hens."

"They don't know what we do."

"They're tryin' to find out."

Goose flesh rose along the back of Sam's neck. Before, he had never thought about the right or wrong of slavery. He had been born to what Southerners called their "institution"; he simply had lived with the fact that colored people were owned by whites. But if Uncle Dan'l ever ran away, Sam couldn't conceive of John Quarles hiring professional slave chasers to track him down. Slave-chasing was a gruesome game in which human hunters went after human prey. It was nasty, and it gave Sam a creepy feeling. Ma had told

him how awful it was for Cain to kill Abel, and he couldn't
see how slave-chasing was any different, except that Cain
had been forced to bag his quarry without dogs and a gun.

Bence merely shrugged when he heard about the slave
chasers. "When that pair moves on, others'll follow. Mebbe
it'll be that way all summer, but they'll never find Jim."

"And that's a good thing for you," Sam said. "They'd
hang you sure."

Tom chuckled. "Pap'd be pleased if there was a price on
Bence's head. Then he could claim that old Bence had
amounted to somethin'."

Even Bence grinned, but the surly look that was more
natural returned. "First they'd have to catch me," he said.
"An' they couldn't. Nobody round Hannibal knows the
river or hills or cave or bottoms the way I do."

Yet Bence wasn't taking foolish chances. When they
shoved off in another borrowed skiff, Bence warned, "Don't
say nothin'—not even in a whisper. Voices carry at night,
farther'n you think. They could follow us just by the sound."

Sam and Tom nodded silently. A bright moon rode high
over Hannibal, stars studded the sky, and the river stretched
before them, so well lighted that they could see the bulky
shadows marking the Illinois shore. Bence loaded the boat
with firewood, as he had promised Jim.

In the stillness, as the skiff bounced over the water, Sam
strained his ears for the sound of pursuers. Then, approaching the Illinois side, he listened even harder, for slave chasers
could hide here in the darkness of the river bank. When they
at last reached the bottoms, Sam breathed more easily, certain that they had made the passage without being detected.

Jim waited for them at the edge of the island. They anchored the skiff in a sequestered cove and carted the wood
to where, about midway on that marshy strip, Jim had cleared
a space. Soon a fire crackled, potatoes roasted, the spareribs

sizzled. Jim insisted on sharing his feast. "If you'll eat wid a colored man," he added.

"Not many whites ask me to dinner," Bence said with a chuckle.

Sam studied the strapping, hard-muscled slave. Jim possessed a quick, infectious laugh that the boy liked, and clear, black eyes that were steady and unafraid, and a mouth that reflected stout resolution. Yet for all his size, Jim's movements were like his manners and his speech—slow, deliberate, easygoing, gentle. Sam had a feeling that the Negro could handle a baby or a giant and never harm either.

"Jim," Sam asked, his curiosity getting the best of him, "did they use you bad on that plantation?"

"Not bad, no. Dey work me hard, but Ah don't mind dat."

"Were you sold away from your Ma and Pa?"

"Ah 'sposes so. But Ah don't ever knowed dem. If'n Ah step by mistake on some po' man, an' he say, 'Jim, is dis any way to use you po' ole Pappy?' Ah wouldn't knowed who 'twas till he tole me."

"Then why *did* you run away?"

Jim stirred up the fire, gnawed on a sparerib, and tried to put his thoughts in order. Then he said, "Ah reckon Ah did it from thinkin' 'bout how a bird jus' born learns to fly off by hisself, an' how an ole wolf train her cub so he kin do his own chicken-stealin', an' how white chillun growed up an' say good-by to dere folks an' strike out on dere own. Dat's how God planned de world. Every creature was to have his chance to be free, an' see how he kin make out by hisself, an' laugh at hisself fo' bein' a fool or give hisself a pat on de back an' say, 'Boy, you ain't so bad, considerin'.' You see how it is?"

"Not before, but *now* I do," Sam said. The gentleness in Jim was like the gentleness in Uncle Dan'l.

"So dat's how it is," Jim went on. "Ah say to myself, 'Jim,

you big fool, why-all you ain't free lak God intend?' An'
Ah say to myself, 'Jim, you no-good cotton picker, you got
to be free 'cause God's gwine to raise one dash-dang ruckus
if you come nosin' round hebben widout even tryin'.' So
one mornin' Ah woke up an' took off, an' hyar Ah is!"

Jim threw back his head and laughed. Then he licked the
dripping end of another sparerib.

"He ain't never goin' to be a slave again," Bence said
savagely.

Jim nodded. "Ah make me dat pledge."

"An' Jim's word is better'n some white people who stand
up in court an' swear on the Bible that they're tellin' the
truth," Bence said.

Sam poked the fire. "If those people ever read in those
Bibles, maybe Jim wouldn't have to run away."

"The preachers say what the slaveowners want to hear,"
Tom said.

"An' the judges use the laws the way the slaveowners tell
'em to," Bence growled.

Jim cackled gleefully. "You know how come dese ribs
taste so good? Dey's *free* ribs!"

10.
Jim

ALL THROUGH THE SUMMER, slave chasers kept passing through Hannibal. Sometimes there would be only one or two, sometimes a dozen. Tom and Sam hung around the dock, the stores, the taverns, keeping these human bloodhounds under surveillance and learning how much they knew. Often inquiries were made about a slave named Jim who had been tracked this far before he disappeared.

Tom couldn't resist plaguing the slave chasers. He would listen to the thoroughly accurate description they gave of Jim, nod his head and say, "Yes, sir, that's the one—saw him hidin' behind some casks of tobacco when the *Jeanie Deans* pulled out'n here for Cairo a day or so ago. If'n you want to get him, you better scoot 'cause out of Cairo he could get clear to the Atlantic."

The chaser scooted, leaving his partner to follow the leads on other runaways. Another time Tom sent the searchers toward St. Louis, swearing he'd seen Jim riding off that way under a load of hay. Sam laughed each time Tom's game worked, but Tom outsmarted himself. He gave one chaser a full description of how to find the copper cylinder in the cave and declared he knew for a fact Jim was living there. The fellow stomped back into Hannibal, cut, bruised, scared

out of his wits by the bats and the face of the cadaver, and determined to skin Tom alive if he ever laid hands on him.

"Guess the sport's over till he gets out'n town," Tom said sadly.

But Bence was furious. "He may figure you were tryin' to throw him off a-purpose. He'll guess then that you do know somethin' an' shadow you an' let you lead him straight to Jim."

Bence looked as though he would beat Tom good, but Sam said, "Don't jump in over your head, reaching conclusions."

"If'n that fellow should catch Jim . . ."

"He hasn't yet, Bence."

Tom had never been able to handle Bence the way Sam could now. It wasn't only that Sam spoke up to Bence, but he did it as though Bence were his equal and so ought to have better sense. More, he treated Jim in the same manner. Maybe that was what had really won over Bence.

At least twice a week the two boys and Bence sailed over to the bottoms to see Jim. When they could scrounge food enough, they all ate together. Other times they watched Jim eat. They understood toward mid-August how the days were dragging for the Negro. He acted restless, was almost short-tempered, and talked more and more about taking the big chance on breaking out and getting to Canada, where he'd really be free.

"Not yet," Bence said quietly. "Those slave chasers'll go snoopin' somewhere else in a little while. Then you can go safely."

"Dat's whut you allers say."

"Don't big-lip me," Bence growled. "I could turn you in an' go on a spree to New Orleans. Mebbe I should afore the hounds catch you an' tear your worthless black hide to pieces."

But Bence was never going to turn him in, and Jim knew it. "Ain't money enuff to buy your heart," Jim said.

"Pap don't give me no heart," Bence grumbled. "He sneaked in a whisky bottle instead. Blood goes in one end an' comes out t'other corn likker. That's why I'm no good." Bence laughed. "Only thing ever brung Pap to Missouri was the fact he heard the likker was cheap. Guess frontiers never would get settled if it weren't for dirt-cheap rotgut to draw men like Pap. They come a'runnin' an' that beats down the trail for respectable folks to follow. Now ain't that so, Sam?"

"Sounds mighty reasonable, Bence," Sam agreed with a laugh.

Jim grinned and the argument ended. Before Bence left, he tossed a knife to the Negro. "Here, try a little whittlin'. Clears your mind better'n anything."

Sam never confessed to anyone the battle he was having with himself over Jim. After all, Pa was the justice of the peace, enforcing the law was his business, and here was his son breaking the law practically under his own roof. To make Sam's struggle harder, the Judge seemed to suffer a long spell of bad health, more than likely because he was worried over his debts and the possibility that he might have to dispose of the Tennessee land at a pittance, after all.

Sam hinted at his problem to Ma, but not so she could ever guess that he was condoning the harboring of a fugitive slave.

"You think slavery's right, Ma?"

"Why, I hardly ever think about it, Sammy."

"I know—but when you do?"

"You read all the time in the papers what happens to those poor runaway slaves when they reach Canada. They're not used to those awful snows, Sammy, nor having to earn their own living or care for their own families, which, heaven knows, is difficult enough for white people like us. So I'm not surprised to read that those slaves become despondent in Canada and would give anything to be back on a Southern plantation again."

"Maybe the slaveowners write that hogwash."

Jane Clemens didn't try to control her exasperation. "Sammy, I've got worries enough without you picking an argument with me."

"Do you believe in hanging abolitionists and such like?" Sam persisted, stubborn to the core.

"Ask your father. He knows all about the law."

"Of course, lawyers believe in hanging. That's what makes their business."

"Sammy, do stop talking like that," Jane Clemens cried, her impatience turning to real anger, and Sam ducked out of the kitchen thinking that he didn't care. No matter what Ma and Pa believed, Jim deserved his chance to be free.

If Sam had possessed a lingering doubt, it disappeared next

morning. At the dock a white overseer was waiting for the steamer south, and the way the man spoke to his slave— snappish and mean as though the overseer lived with constant indigestion—disgusted Sam. Poor old John Hannicks, the drayman who was a free Negro by his master's will, forgot to look for the first smudge of smoke beyond the point. Hannicks muttered angrily to his horse, glowered at the overseer, and opened and closed long, restless fingers. The flustered slave stumbled over a carpetbag, tried to catch his balance, and sprawled on the dock. The overseer spun around, seized a large chunk of iron ore in a rage, and flung it at the fallen Negro. Unhappily his aim was good.

Sam turned away, sickened. He couldn't cry. He was too tight inside, too aghast at the sight of brutality. He wouldn't use a dog or a horse or a pig like that. Within an hour the slave was dead.

"It's murder," Sam told old Hannicks. "They ought to take that man and string him to a tree."

The drayman moaned in a mournful voice. "Dey won't. 'Most everybody in Hannibal feel lak you do—dat it's wrong an' should be punished, mebbe wid a hangin' lak you say— but dey won't do nothin'."

"They've got laws!"

"An' dat's it, Sammy. De system won't let 'em. A slave's jus' property. A man want to destroy his'n property, dat's his business!"

Sam felt sick again. Maybe Ma and Pa could understand now that there were worse fates than freezing in Canada.

Bence and Tom soon heard about the murder Sam had seen. The news seemed to sweep over Hannibal, sobering everyone's spirit and making people smile briefly and then look away when they met. "It ain't that they feel so shocked this has happened," Bence said, filled with his old malice. "It's only one such murder in Hannibal, an' they never 'spect

to see another like it. But underneath they feel guilty, an'
if you plague 'em about it they'll turn on you an' wish you
were the one who had been killed!"

"Jim's restless enough now," Tom said. "I hope he won't
hear about this. It'll be like a nettle under his skin."

Bence nodded soberly. "Don't either of you blabbermouths
say nothin'," he growled.

They sailed over to see Jim that afternoon. The Negro
jumped up, overjoyed they had come, and with ill-concealed
pride showed them the canoe he had carved from a piece of
kindling wood. The replica was perfect in every detail, and
Tom and Sam both examined it enviously while Jim broke
into an unhappy sweat wondering how he could divide one
little canoe. Then Jim detected the longing in Bence's eyes.
If Jim had thought for a thousand years, he never would
have guessed that a toy could appeal to Bence. With a flood
of relief the runaway cried, "Ah made it fo' you, Bence, if
mebbe you'd lak it."

"What'd I do with it?" Bence growled. But he took the
replica, grinning at the two small seats and tiny paddle, and
later Sam saw him secretly rubbing it with his hands and
casting covert glances at it from time to time. Once Tom
snatched at it; Bence kicked his hand away, and Tom rolled
over in the grass, whimpering.

"Why you do dat?" Jim asked, surprised and puzzled.

Bence grumbled, "He ain't as hurt as he makes out," and
put the canoe in his pocket so that neither he nor Tom would
be tempted to act that way again. Afterward Bence continued to rub his hand on the outside of his pocket. The
gesture could have revealed nervousness or embarrassment.

Jim sang spirituals. The Negro's deep, ringing baritone
voice seemed to circle around them, and to blend them into
his songs as he appeared lost in the music. The sadness of

the spirituals became his sadness—and Sam's sadness, and Tom's and Bence's. Jim stopped all at once, caught in the old fit of restlessness. "Ah ain't stayin' here much longer," he told Bence.

"Mebbe in another week, Jim. Mebbe sooner. Don't see many slave chasers round here any more. They all go down the same rat hole, I guess."

"You take me to solid ground on the Illinois shore. Ah make it from dere."

"I'll do better'n that," Bence promised. "I'll sail you up the river one night to where I know you'll be safe."

"De underground railroad run through part of Illinois."

"That's what I mean."

Jim stood up, the tallest man Sam had ever seen. He stirred up the fire, then picked up a stone and gave it a heave, as though trying to rid himself of something. Distantly a splash came back to them.

"It won't be longer den a week, Bence?"

"Dash-dang, didn't I say so?"

"Now don't get mad at me."

"You make me mad."

"You know Ah don't mean to."

Bence scowled, but Sam smiled. The gentleness in Jim was always there, no more than a pin scratch from the surface.

Sailing back to the Missouri shore Sam spoke in a way that upset Bence. "Next time we go to that island," Sam said, "maybe Jim won't be there."

"Shut up."

"It's just a hunch."

"Then swallow your hunch."

"But lookit, Bence, Jim isn't really free till he gets away. He feels caged up, and I wouldn't blame him if he just took off without waiting for you."

Across Bence's face stole about as ugly an expression as Sam had ever noticed. "If'n he did that—well, he just better not."

"You don't own Jim."

Bence turned on Sam with a snarl. "You say that again, an' I'll brain you with an oar!"

"Likely I'd deserve it," Sam admitted, and Bence appeared satisfied.

Walking up the road afterward, Bence once more took the toy canoe from his pocket and rubbed his fingers along its soft, smooth sides.

Before a week had passed, on a late August day when Hannibal settled into the drowsiest sort of summer lethargy, Tom told Sam that Bence planned to take Jim up the river that night.

"Bence's goin' all by himself," Tom said.

"I knew he would."

"He said not to expect him for a couple of days at least."

"I can sleep with my fingers crossed for two nights."

In bed that evening Sam looked out the window at the moon and the millions of stars off in a space so big nobody could calculate its size. Somewhere on the silent river Jim and Bence skimmed the edges of the tree shadows in a skiff. Likely Bence had been watching the tide and knew it would be right tonight.

In a way, Sam thought, his summer had begun one night musing on how much fifty dollars would mean to Ma and Pa. He was a lot older now than he had been those few weeks ago. There wasn't anything more important on earth than being free—that wisdom Jim had taught him. And there wasn't any sense judging a person till you could know what he was like underneath—that wisdom Bence had taught him. And you couldn't let other people decide right from wrong for you, because you had to feel in your heart what was right and know in your mind what was wrong—and that wisdom he had taught himself. So, presently, Sam dozed off, smiling at the dream of Bence and Jim far up the Illinois shore, making contact with the underground railroad.

The dream ended abruptly. Sam sat up as though an un-identified fear had bounced him on a spring. Deep night sur-rounded him. And then he heard the call that Tom often gave beneath the window.

Sam didn't have to be told that there must be some kind of desperate trouble. He bolted into his clothes and out onto the shed roof. Both Bence and Tom were waiting when Sam slid softly to the ground.

"Bence couldn't find him," Tom cried.

"You mean Jim was gone? From the island?"

"I came back to get you two to help me search through the bottoms," Bence said in almost a sob.

Bence had left the skiff tied to the steamboat dock. Tom handled the tiller, and Bence shook out the sail until it was bellying in a brisk breeze.

"You search all over that island?" Sam asked.

"There ain't much of her to search. The moonlight's good, an' I covered every inch of that strip. Jim ain't there."

"Did you call, in case Jim was hiding in the water?"

"I even swam around myself."

"It's funny all right."

"It's mean," Bence said, suddenly growlish. "Jim should'a waited."

Sam declared that now Bence sounded like a fool. Jim had promised to wait another week for Bence, and Jim was the kind who kept his word—if he could. "Don't you see, Bence? Some noise must have alarmed him and sent him scurrying."

"Like someone gettin' lost in that part of the bottoms?"

"Or a slave chaser who found his way in by luck."

"Mebbe," Bence admitted. "He could'a took off like that. Ain't too many other places either he could'a hid."

"We'll search 'em all if necessary."

"Some of 'em are far apart. The water's deep an' covers trees in places that's still got branches stickin' out. Roots, too, can wrap round your legs. It's tricky swimmin'." Bence mumbled his words, as though thinking aloud. At the tiller Tom felt suddenly chilled, and Sam frowned uncomfortably.

"Bence, how much longer do you figure it is before daybreak?" he asked.

"Two or three hours."

"Lookin' will be easier then."

"When we find him, he'll have to wait till tomorrer night for me to take him up the Illinois shore." Bence swore. "He better have a good reason, puttin' me to all this extra trouble."

Tom swung the skiff around, bearing toward the bottoms. A bright moon, a million stars seemed the sole witnesses to the drama on the old river. The occupants of the boat lapsed into silence as though each had crawled into his own thoughts, his own theories, his own apprehensions. Tall marsh grass brushed the side of the skiff.

"Watch where you're goin'," Bence blustered at Tom. Again, silence.

Sam believed implicitly that they would find Jim hiding on another island, and that after Bence had cussed his head off, Jim would have a sensible explanation for his flight. Off in the distance an old hoot owl despaired of his weary existence. They skirted the edge of a beaver dam, and, Sam supposed humorously, the curses of the beavers turned the water blue.

"Bear off to the left," Bence growled at Tom. "That'll bring us to the island nearest the one where we left him."

"Don't you think we ought to go to the other island?" Sam asked. "Jim could've returned."

Bence hesitated, then conceded the point by shouting at Tom, "Why are you bearin' left when we're goin' to the other island first?"

"You didn't tell me."

"An' you can't think nothin' out for yourself. You'll be like Pap, decidin' it's easier to likker up 'n ever make anything out'n yourself!"

Tom held his temper, knowing Bence was keyed up and his insults meant nothing. Anyhow, Tom almost had rammed that beaver dam, and how Bence would have blistered him then!

Sam recognized the bulky shadow of the island they had visited so often, looming in the moonlight. They ran around it to the old point of anchorage, and Sam said, "Let me search with you this time, Bence."

But neither found any trace of Jim. "Not even a shavin' from the canoe he carved," Bence grumbled. "We'd have saved time if we bore left in the first place."

It took them about five minutes to cross to the next strip of habitable marsh. A good swimmer might have made it in fifteen. Except for geese and brant there didn't seem to be any reason for this land existing. In daylight they could have seen Jim wasn't there, Bence growled afterward.

"It'll be daybreak soon enough," Sam said.

"Ain't been out here since I went huntin' 'bout this time of day last fall," Bence muttered.

"How'd you make out?"

"Better'n I'm doin' now."

Tom said, with a kind of nervous laugh, "Geese come south through here from Canada, an' the slaves go north."

"You shut up an' mind the tiller," Bence shouted, mad at the joke.

A distance that took ten minutes to cross separated the second marsh strip from the third. Almost the first thing

Sam recognized on the island were the remnants of a duck-blind. The strip was larger than either of the others, but Sam supposed that the duckblind explained why Bence hadn't chosen it for a hide-out. Too many people knew about it.

All three searched this time. Along most of one side there were nests of water moccasins, but Bence beat off the snakes with a piece of driftwood. Around them the sky was now pinkening as the sun stretched its arms and yawned at the start of a new day. Bence still wasn't satisfied after they had circled the island without finding Jim. He went around once more, using the same club to beat the water moccasins out of his path, and coming back at last with a dark, worried sullenness in his eyes. "I don't like it, Sam."

"There are more islands."

"Yeah, but there's that lousy stretch of deep water with the trees. Ain't any better'n a nasty morass after awhile."

"Could you swim it?"

"Sure."

"Then why couldn't Jim?"

"Who said he couldn't?" Bence flared. "I'd a-done better without comin' back for you an' Tom."

Sam had wondered why Bence had come back. Halfway across the next open water, daylight overtook them. Home in Hannibal the old cocks would be crowing, the birds singing, John Hannicks waking up and feeding the miserable sway-backed horse that pulled his dray. Here there were steaming surface mists, the eerie screech of some fool loon, the flutter through the water of a catfish with an empty belly.

Bence trimmed the sail till the skiff seemed to drag through the water. He kept his head over the rail, staring intently. "We're right over those trees," he murmured.

Sam, shivering all over, knew then why Bence had come

back for Tom and him. Bence didn't want to be alone if he found what he feared he might.

They had reached the morass when they came on Jim. Bence took an oar and pushed the drowned Negro from under the root of the tree that had pinned him. Jim had probably struggled desperately, trying to free himself in the darkness, but there had been a limit to even his great strength. Sam helped to haul the dead body into the skiff, and Bence tore up part of a sail and covered his friend.

"They never got him," Tom said. "He died free—like he said he would."

"Ain't nobody need pray over him, even if anybody would," Bence said. "Sam, don't you go mumbling the hypocritical talk of the preachers who was all against him!"

"I gotta say good-by in my own way, Bence."

"Well, say it silent."

Tom watched Bence sharply. From a pocket Bence slipped the little canoe Jim had carved.

"You put that in the water, Bence, an' you'll lose it sure."

"You shut up," Bence retorted viciously. "It's his, ain't it? What'd he want more'n to set it free?"

That night Bence disappeared, and Hannibal didn't see him again for three months.

11.

Printer's Devil

FOR SAM, the next months were ones of tremendous change. Everyone asked questions about finding Jim's body in the Illinois bottoms, but he put off all such busybodies with short answers. Meanwhile the ever-continuing financial struggle of the Clemenses forced them to move into an apartment over Orville Grant's drugstore at the southwest corner of Hill and Main, and with a brave effort at cheerfulness, Jane Clemens turned to supplementing the family's meager income by boarding the Grants.

Sam didn't mind the change especially. Dr. Grant's house had style, and its white pilasters and classic Greek-revival dignity stood out among the cheaper dwellings that huddled together all along Main Street like cramped old people seeking company in their common misery. The Judge grumbled that he supposed the Tennessee land must go now, even if it fetched no more than ten cents an acre, but the elder Clemens exerted no effort beyond falling into a fit of despair at this prospect.

Dr. Grant spoke proudly of his home. "Now look at the fine timber in this house, Sammy," the druggist said. "Those pillars were cut up river, and were supposed to be shipped to Marion City where a Colonel Muldrow thought he was going to build a grand metropolis. Well, as it turned out, all the colonel owned was a lot of swampy bottoms, and I got his timber shipped down to Hannibal."

At least Sam could draw one moral from the tale. His father wasn't the only dreamer along the Missouri border. And even with the wolf panting on the Clemens doorstep, the Judge seemed to regain his fight after a time. His springtime ailments that he called "sun pains" and dosed with box after box of pills had abated, and, in rather chipper spirits, he decided to try a fling at politics by announcing himself a candidate for the office of Clerk of the Circuit Court. Six other candidates opposed him.

"It means two dollars for an entry fee, and money for the weekly advertisements in the papers," said Jane Clemens, the practical member of the family.

"I'll be elected," he replied, almost gay in his confidence.

So the Clemenses skimped and somehow found the money. The Judge surprised them. This time his dream possessed feet that walked on the ground. Soon all political parties favored him, and Sam read glowing praise of his father as a steady, honest man who deserved to be elected. Jane Clemens hummed around her new kitchen. When the Judge won his office, the prospects for the Clemens family would brighten considerably, and for once their hopes seemed closer at hand than the fortune that one day would be theirs from the Tennessee land.

Pa's sprightly confidence, Ma's bright, sunny smile sent Sam back to school in good humor. Also he was cheered by the fact that he was finished with cross old Cross. True, Dawson, his new schoolmaster, could handle a switch adeptly, but only under extreme compulsion. Soon after the term at Dawson's started, Sam found himself watching with increasing interest the girl who lived in the neat two-story cottage not more than an easy stone's throw from the old Clemens house. Sam had to admit the truth: Laura Hawkins, who had grown up like most weeds, stringy in the middle and fuzzy on top, had turned all at once into a looker! Fun and humor shone in her blue eyes. Her yellow hair, plaited into two long tails, dangled, pert and pretty, as Laura walked to school in a white frock and embroidered pantalets. Sam made a habit of waiting at the corner and carrying her books, and he answered her questions about Jim.

Sam's puppy love turned Will Bowen's stomach. Jimmy McDaniel, who felt Laura had spurned him for Sam, swore that Sam had no decency.

Sam was the best speller at Dawson's, and the medal old Dawson gave every week to the winner of the school spelling bee could have been Sam's until Hannibal froze over. The limit to Sam's degradation came the Friday that he misspelled a word everyone believed he knew, just so Laura could win the medal.

"Fancy-pants Sammy!" sneered Will.

"Punk!" Jimmy leered, flashing all his decaying teeth.

Sam didn't care. Laura's eyes sparkled at the possession of the medal. But she scolded Sam none the less. "They say you cheated so I could win."

"Maybe I did."

Laura stomped her foot. "Honest, Sam Clemens, if I thought you'd cheated I'd never speak to you again!"

"Well, catfish and kittens," Sam exploded, "ain't you the hoity-toity one!"

"Sam Clemens, don't you talk to me like that!"

"Girls are more trouble than guinea pigs even," Sam stormed in a sudden passion. "I should'a known! Once on the farm I went to school in Florida with my cousin Puss. An' there was a girl there asked, 'Sam Clemens, do you use terbacker?' meaning did I chew it, an' when I said no, she said 'Haw!' and cried out, smart-aleck like, 'Come see this silly boy who ain't ever chawed terbacker.' So I chewed her rotten terbacker an' took sick for most two days, an' that should'a learned me what to expect when you try to please a girl!"

Laura Hawkins heard him through, her blue eyes smoldering. "Well!" she cried, snapping her pigtails like a pair of buggy whips. "I guess I know now the kind of boy you are!" And Laura walked up the hill to her own house, never once looking back.

"Notice you kept the medal," Sam called after her maliciously. "But next week I'll win it back just like that!" And he snapped his fingers.

Next morning, he set off for school with his nose in the air. At the corner Laura waited with her books. "Good morning, Sammy."

"Good morning, Laura."

How could he make sense out of actions like this? Yet it wasn't mannerly to walk on, even if she deserved it. But Sam skipped off with Will Bowen after school that day, leaving Laura to hoist her own books home.

Nobody had to tell Sam that his moods and attitudes these days oozed around inside him like so many jellyfish. He couldn't seem to stay in one course, but veered with every wind. With Tom and Bence, while they shielded Jim during the summer, he had felt almost as grown-up as Orion, and maybe even Pa. And with Laura Hawkins he knew that it was time he filed down some of the rough edges on the razorback rowdy he used to be, living only from one wild prank to the next. Then he would go off with Will, who hadn't changed much at all, and Sam would feel a lust for deviltry rising in him. He slipped into the old familiar mood with no more than a quick sigh and a happy grin.

On Sunday Sam and Will tramped up Holliday's Hill. A cold, frosty day invigorated their spirits. Will remembered how in other years they had worked off their grudge for being forced to attend Sunday school by rolling big stones down the hill and frightening the people who were driving to church. "Now that was good sport," he declared.

"Best ever."

"Sam, it's almost time for those churchgoers to be comin' along."

"You know that spot, Will, where the bushes are, an' nobody ever saw us?"

The other nodded. "Those stones used to go down that hill like they were fired out of cannons!"

"You had to be as accurate as a cannoneer," Sam said with a chuckle. "You had to calculate your distance just right, so that the stone would hit the road 'fore the team of horses got there. 'Member how those horses would plunge, an' the ladies grab their hats, an' the men let out with a stream of words they never learned from the Bible?"

Will hee-hawed. "Sam, we ought to do it again!"

"I don't see why not, considerin' folks has forgot to expect it these days!"

The sport never had been better than on that Sunday. Churchgoing horses by the dozen reared up at the stones whistling before them. Churchgoing ladies by the two dozen grabbed their hats and kicked up their petticoats. And churchgoing men, fat ones and skinny ones, bearded ones and cleanshaven ones, grabbed at the reins and cracked their whips and waved their fists and filled the air with imprecations that, Sam said, luckily never got as far as church.

"Will, I love you for rememberin' this," Sam chortled. "You always was a whiz at it!"

Flattery affected Will's head as air does a blowfish, and his heart yearned now for a grand coup. His glance fell on a rock almost as big as a buggy that needed just a start to send it hurtling down the hill. "Down the road a piece," he said, "I noticed picks and shovels that the quarrymen left." Sam couldn't deny the glorious spectacle the mammoth boulder, crashing down the hill and smashing across the road a hundred yards or so before a wagonload of unsuspecting churchgoers, would make. "We might even get the preacher," he said, adding his own dash to Will's inspiration. "A deacon, anyhow."

Unloosening the boulder was much more difficult than either boy had imagined. They came again the following Sunday, bringing Jimmy McDaniel and Johnny Briggs as helpers. On the third Sunday, Tom joined the recruits. They sweated at the backbreaking work, then all at once the boulder tipped forward and started to roll.

"Look out, boys, she's coming!" Sam shouted, just as Johnny Briggs handed Will a pick. Will jumped back, missing by seconds being flattened like a pancake.

"Look at her go!" Tom cried breathlessly.

They couldn't believe it. The boulder flashed along, the way a comet streaks across the sky. Full in its path, about halfway down the hill, stood a tree. The boulder cut it down as a scythe cuts wheat. "That tree changed her course a little," Sam cried, his voice trembling as he eyed the old Negro who was coming down the road in a cart.

The poor man saw the boulder descending on him. He lashed the horse with his whip. Terror spread his eyes into saucers. The boulder was making gigantic leaps now, kicking up a cloud of dust whenever it struck the ground, filling the air with flying fragments. The horrified colored man lashed in a frenzy. The old cart rocked crazily. The horse foamed at the mouth.

Sam—his mouth gaping, heart pounding, knees fluttering —stood paralyzed as the boulder smashed onto a rock ledge that cropped out over the road. Suddenly it sailed into the air—over the Negro and the cart, over the road—and buried itself in the soft dirt on the other side. No one troubled to dig it out for the next forty years.

"That was a whistler," Will mumbled.

"That wasn't fun!" Sam said. "Let's get out of here before someone catches us. I'm sick of this place anyhow."

Sam knew that he was changing and had dash-dang better change. One day he looked at Henry and discovered that his younger brother had grown out of his irritating singsong ways, if not his pesky ones. The boys ended in a fight that tore open two pillows and covered the bedroom with goose feathers. Ma stormed in on them, mad as a hornet. "When your Pa gets back from that lawsuit he's attending in Palmyra," she said, "I'll have him lace you both!"

But they never received the lickings. It was raw March now. The Judge rode home through a driving sleet storm, chilled to the marrow of his bones, and Ma helped the numb, shivering man into bed. Pleurisy developed into pneumonia. Ma, red-eyed, trusted blindly in Dr. Meredith.

"That old harpooner just stands around while Pa grows weaker and weaker," Sam blustered.

Jane Clemens took the boy in her arms and held him close without scolding. "Oh, Sammy, there's so much trouble in the world!"

"Ma, why do we get it all?"

"We don't, Sammy—not really. Think of poor Injun Joe —he was lost in the cave and living on bats when they found him last week."

Orion came home from St. Louis. Pamela sat by her father's bed all day and wept. In high fever, the Judge moaned; in rational moments he told them over and over, "The Tennessee land, the Tennessee land—cling to it, and some day it'll make you rich."

Sam, Henry, and Orion huddled together in the bedroom. Jane Clemens rocked to and fro in a chair. She didn't weep like Pamela, not even when the Presbyterian minister began to pray. Pa motioned to Pamela, pulled her head down to his lips, and whispered, "Let me die." Orion placed his arms around both of the younger boys, and they all clung together.

Pa's death dazed them all. Henry, red-eyed, like Pamela, said little. Jane Clemens told Orville Grant, "He was such a good man—kind and warmhearted." Then one night, she awoke, frightened out of her wits, to see Sam, wrapped in a bedsheet, walking along the hall.

"Sammy!" she cried.

"Yes, Ma?" Sam answered. But he didn't realize that he spoke, for he had reverted to the old habit of walking in his sleep. The boy repeated this disturbing performance for several nights.

Sam's sleep-walking stemmed then, as always, from an acute conscience that invariably plagued him in times of stress. At the Judge's death Sam broke down completely, bedeviled by pangs of guilt over his wildness, his disobedience, his indifference to his father's wishes, which must have been a constant source of unhappiness to the dead man.

Jane Clemens could not bear the sight of her son's misery. "It's all right, Sammy," she said gently. "What's done is done, and it doesn't matter to Pa any more. But I want you to make me a promise—"

"Anything!" Sam wailed. "Just don't make me go to school any more, and I'll promise anything!"

In spite of her troubles, Jane Clemens was still capable of smiling. How much like her Sammy, attaching a bargain to his offer to turn over a new leaf! But she said soberly, "Sammy, if you go back to school, I'm afraid it can only be for a little while. So promise me to be a better boy. Promise not to break my heart."

Sam declared solemnly that henceforth he would be faith-

ful and industrious and upright—like Pa. His vows were
sacred to him. He hoped that God would strike him dead
if he didn't carry them out.

"I'm not Tom Blankenship," Jane Clemens said. "I know
you mean it, Sammy. I won't make you prick your finger
and squeeze out drops of blood to prove it."

Afterward Sam realized that Ma knew a great deal more
than she ever let on.

With the Judge dead, the Clemenses still had to live.
Orion, who was now a very good book and job printer receiving the excellent wages of ten dollars a week, returned
to St. Louis, promising Ma that he would send her three
dollars every payday. Pamela also rallied in the emergency.
Accomplished at playing the piano and guitar, Pamela jour-
neyed fifty miles to the town of Paris and set herself up as
a teacher of music. Whatever was left from her earnings
after paying her board she sent home to Hannibal. Sam
thought of poor Pamela, timid as a mouse and scarcely any
stronger, and realized that she possessed a lion's heart to
strike out this way. "Ma," he said, "not many girls would
do it."

"All my children are helping in a way that would have
made your father burst with pride," Jane Clemens declared.

"Have you thought that maybe we could sell the Tennessee land?"

"No, Sammy—not yet. We're getting along."

Pa himself would have said just that. He had tutored Ma
well. There never was a family, Sam guessed, that could
surpass the Clemenses for nibbling on a crust of bread while
they dreamed of a day when they would live in the lap of
luxury. They were like a skinny old lady with her head
stuck up a stovepipe, looking over the fine clothes she had
stored away in the attic. It didn't matter if, while she looked,
her bare feet froze solid to the ground.

Then a day came when Jane Clemens talked seriously to Sam about his future. Since Orion had done so well as a printer, the trade seemed a good one for Sam to follow. Joseph P. Ament, a recent arrival in Hannibal from Palmyra, planned to re-establish his Democratic weekly newspaper here. Ma proposed what had already been decided in her own mind—it would be fine if Sam went to work as an apprentice on Mr. Ament's *Missouri Courier*.

"Will I have to live away from home, Ma?"

"As an apprentice, Sammy, you'll live with the Aments; but we'll all be close, and we can visit whenever we want."

"Will I get wages like Orion?"

"At first, while you're learning your trade, Mr. Ament will give you clothes and board."

"Same as though I was a slave," Sam said, but he accepted his fate cheerfully.

So on the following Monday Sam arrived at the Aments. Mrs. Ament looked down her rail of a nose at the new printer's devil, while Sam stared back defiantly at this tall, thin, flat-chested Yankee female who gave the impression that she sipped vinegar for breakfast.

"Well, here's your suit," Mrs. Ament said in a pinched voice that seemed to come out of her throat like a sulky wisp of smoke through a sooty chimney.

Sam caught the suit of Mr. Ament's hand-me-downs that his freshly adopted mistress flung across the room. He held it up, looked it over critically, and pronounced with judicial gravity, "Thank you, ma'am. I reckon it'll fit me 'bout as good as a circus tent."

"Don't be sassy, young Clemens," Mrs. Ament snapped, breaking through the soot in an angry puff. "They're the best we have."

"I guess you'll feed me so I'll grow into them," Sam said, knowing the old girl wasn't much of a match.

Mrs. Ament tossed her head—something she better not try too often, Sam thought, unless she wanted to snap it off her neck and crash it through a window. "You'll eat in the kitchen with the cook and her mulatto girl!" And having discharged the duty of receiving her husband's latest apprenticed ragamuffin, Mrs. Ament sneezed up her sleeve— an affectation that made Sam laugh. He could see that she saved just about everything for a rainy day.

Unknown to Sam, his interview with Mrs. Ament had been observed by an amiable young giant somewhere around the age of seventeen or eighteen, who was so hemmed in by the castoff clothes he was wearing, that any quick cough might send pants and coat flying to opposite poles of the globe. But the reckless and debonair Wales McCormack, Esq., who added the title to his name in the belief that a man who owned his own soul possessed all the property he needed, felt himself the master in any situation. Upon Sam he bestowed a look carefully balanced between sympathy and contempt, and then, so that Sam would know from the start that he had been well educated in language in the poor man's college of a printing office, he said all in one gulp, "Well, it's a fretful, peevish, cross-grained, ill-tempered, sour-natured, scolding, obscure little brat old Ament's saddled himself with this trip!"

"Pleased to meet you," Sam said, recognizing the breed at once.

"Boy, watch your step with me—I can swear in nine languages."

"They only count one at a time."

Wales laughed. "I hope you didn't believe what she said about getting fed in the kitchen. You'll eat there, but you won't feel fed!"

"I can forage," Sam said.

"Now, that's the spirit." Wales cried approvingly. "The

cellar's full of 'taters and onions. You steal 'em, and I'll cook
'em. Since that's settled, come along and I'll introduce you
to our jour printer."

"What's a 'jour'?"

"Journeyman, you fool. Oh, I can see you're a green one
all right." Wales' eyes were suddenly alight with happy anticipations.

The jour printer was Pet McMurray, and he was no beauty.
His auburn locks were greased into slick rolls, a red goatee
hung from his chin like a trimmed-down exclamation point,
and he wore a plug hat tipped so far over his nose that Sam
had to look twice to make certain he had any nose at all.
His mouth was never free of the "Cuba sixes" he smoked
endlessly. When Pet couldn't find work as a printer, Wales
announced, he gave temperance lectures, so he was always
well supplied with money and liquor. It was hard to tell
whether Pet was on or off the bottle, for at any time he
walked with a funny mincing gait, as though he was constantly treading on hot coals. Intuition warned Sam that
whatever Wales claimed would bear thorough investigation,
but in the case of Pet's temperance lectures Wales emerged
with banners of virtue unfurled. Pet had a stack of handbills
already printed, pending the next moment of thirsty emergency.

"Mr. McMurray," Wales announced, "may I introduce
Mr. Clemens—Mr. Sam Clemens, I'll have you know, with
an S as in soft-headed, an A as in asses-ain't-all-from-Arkan-
sas, and an M as in mush-mouth."

"The middle name," said Sam, "is Langhorne. Let's hear
you go through that."

"Tomorrow," Wales demurred.

Pet nodded at Sam. "That's right—keep Wales in his place.
I suppose you're anxious to start work, and I'm all for a
smart boy who's eager to get ahead. Now I'll tell you what

your first job is and I hope you'll hop to it. This place is overrun with type lice. Clean them out of the shop—every last biting varmint of 'em!'"

Sam searched everywhere for half an hour before he caught Pet winking at Wales and Wales snickering behind his hand. Then Sam knew why he had looked in such fretful futility —type lice didn't exist. "It's a hoary joke," Pet confessed, "but we've got worse ones. We thought we'd break you in gently."

Sam couldn't stay peeved long, even though the next day he was sent to the saddler's for "strap oil." Pet and Wales omitted none of the standard rites in initiating an apprentice, but Sam learned quickly. Before long, he even took up smoking Pet's Cuba sixes.

The jour printer never overstrained himself, doing just enough work so that Ament wouldn't drive him back to delivering temperance lectures, and Wales always had the excuse that he could do more if old Ament would buy him a suit that didn't cut down his wind. Both decided that the new printer's devil was a happy addition to the fold. Thanks to the solid education Sam had received from Bence and Tom, he delighted his companions with a song about a poor drunken man; Pet especially adored the line: *If I ever get up again, I'll stay up—if I kin!*

Old Ament, Sam accepted as a "diminutive chunk of human meat," who had promised him two suits of clothes a year but was never going to give him more than one. The fare in the kitchen proved as skimpy as Wales had predicted, and the nightly raids on the cellar as profitable.

"The Aments kind of shake your faith in God," Sam said.

"How come?" Pet asked.

"Well, with lightning so cheap, why ain't the ornery breed wiped out?"

Pet yanked his goatee and declared, "Sammy, you're the dash-dangdest. You oughta go into a minstrel show!"

Sam's days fell into a pattern. Winter mornings, he built the fires, then hopped out into the frosty air for a romp to the neighborhood pump for water. Sweeping the office floor warmed him again and made him drowsy, so that he dragged around, picking up the scattered type and cussing Pet's confounded butterfingers. Next came the ordeal with the hellbox, dumping the pied type on a table and sorting out the broken pieces. He dampened the paper for printing on Sunday, and early each week doused the inking rolls with turpentine and oiled the platen springs on the press. He washed up a form better than Pet, who blessed him for it, for Pet was willing to spend a little flattery to get out of any kind of work. Wales cocked his head, listening to Sam singing "Annie Laurie" or "Along the Beach at Rockaway" as he ran the job press, and nudged Pet. "You'd think, now an' then, he'd slip and at least lose a finger!" he would exclaim. On Thursday the *Missouri Courier* was published, and Sam became manager of distribution—that is, he delivered the paper. But Sam was happy, and printer's ink became a fragrant elixir in his nostrils. He advanced rapidly, learning to set type with creditable skill and to print poems on bits of silk as gifts for Puss and Laura Hawkins. He also earned the dignity of eating in the Aments' dining room.

Sam's hostility toward Ament's wife never sank very far beneath the surface, and he prayed for chances to snipe at her with darts of humor. When coffee was served, he watched the woman stringently doling out the brown sugar, and Pet and Wales waited expectantly as the mischief bubbled up in Sam's eyes. "Lookit there, Mrs. Ament," Sam broke out in an excited voice. "Six extra grains slipped into Wales' cup. You better dock him for that tomorrow."

Mrs. Ament turned and in nettled silence began doling out Sam's brown sugar. "Now you're docking me," he complained bitterly, "and that's not Christian!"

Knowingly Sam had struck a double blow, since Mrs. Ament was both frugal and devoutly religious. "Here, serve yourself," the flustered woman snapped, and Wales swore afterward that, if Sam kept up the teasing, Ament's wife would commit suicide.

"She'd have Ament fire you, but you're too good. He won't let you go," Pet chuckled.

"Not when he doesn't have to pay me wages," Sam grumbled.

Sam reaped yet another compensation in the vistas, opened for him by the *Missouri Courier*, of the world that existed beyond Hannibal. The wires of the new magnetic telegraph now reached into Missouri, and the closing battles of the Mexican War found Sam working furiously to keep up with the rousing dispatches. Cholera and smallpox epidemics traveled the old river, taking distressing tolls. Gold was discovered at Sutter's Mill, the "California Yellow Fever" swept the country, and Sam watched the wagons rolling through Hannibal, bearing jaunty signs:

> Although the road is rough and thorny
> We're on our way to Californy.

The news that filled the columns of Ament's paper was exciting, but it was a vision into a world far removed from his own that truly captivated Sam. He was walking home to see Ma one day when the leaf from a book fluttered before his eyes. Since he now automatically examined any printed matter, Sam stopped. He read every word, and was more moved than he had ever been in his entire life. Tears stung his eyes, his sensitive emotions overflowed, his heart melted with human sympathy. Sam had read a few books, including a novel or two by Sir Walter Scott, and in the copies of the *Southern Literary Messenger* that Ament received on exchange he could read stories by a chap named Edgar Allan Poe. But never had he read anything like this page from a book about Joan of Arc. The passage dealt with the Maid's persecution in prison by her English captors, and Sam put the leaf in his pocket and hurried on. If Henry couldn't tell him where to find the rest of the story, Ma could. Now, Sam had a heroine; Joan of Arc became his ideal, a symbol of human dignity.

"What a fine heretic you'd have made," Wales taunted. "There's no question of it, Sam. You'd have been burned at the stake."

"I expect I would."

"Twice," Pet said. "They'd have made sure of you!"

But after a while, eating roasted potatoes stolen from the Ament cellar and smoking one of Pet's cheroots, Sam would again fill the evening with his humorous lament about the repentant drunkard: *"If I ever get up again, I'll stay up—if I kin!"* Yet, in his way, he was holding to his pledge to Jane Clemens—he was being more faithful and more industrious and more upright than before he had bound his body, if not his soul, to Joseph Ament. At last, Sam guessed, he was beginning to grow up.

Orion knew he would make less money in Hannibal, but he decided to return from St. Louis anyhow, so that he could be nearer Ma. Pamela also came home and when the travel-worn Orion walked through the door, Jane Clemens and Pamela rushed across the room and showered him with kisses. Sam looked on, grinning. Orion appeared dazed. "The dash-dang fool!" Sam muttered to Henry. "It never occurred to Orion anyone could love him!"

12.

Sam and Orion

MA WAS BEHIND Orion's buying a newspaper. Sam didn't understand all the details, except that some friends of Jane Clemens who owned a printing establishment had been smitten by the California Yellow Fever and were burning to let the place go for next to nothing, so that they could rush off to the gold fields. Pamela also joined in this conspiracy to saddle Orion with a responsibility he didn't want. Ma's friends possessed a piano, and since none of the folks who left for California ever realized they might go broke prospecting and wish they could open a dance hall, the instrument was to stay in Hannibal. Didn't Orion think it was wonderful that by borrowing the piano Pamela could be home with Ma and still give her music lessons?

"Trapped," said Orion's gloomy expression, knowing he would try to please everyone but himself. He had returned from St. Louis wanting to find work as a printer and editor with somebody else having to worry over business details. But even from the grave, Pa seemed to be leading Orion around by the nose. The Judge had always dreamed of buying a newspaper for Orion and setting him on the high road to fame, fortune, and independence, Ma said, and that fact clinched the argument for her.

Where the money was coming from Sam hadn't the re-
motest idea. Maybe Orion would borrow it, maybe a tiny
finger of the Tennessee land was to be wrenched from the
hand of future bounty, maybe the money would fall from
heaven. Apparently the money came from somewhere, for
Orion, depressed over the entire transaction, bought his
newspaper. To prove that the Clemens family could never
be satisfied with small dreams, Ma decided to move back to
their old cottage on Hill Street.

"You know what's wrong with Orion?" Sam confided to
Pet and Wales. "He's like a girl, thinking he has to get along
with everybody. Whatever side of an argument he hears
last, that's what he thinks. In politics he's a Whig one week
and a Democrat the next, and if they ever start a Hottentot
Party, he'll switch over to that. Let a cat walk by and meow,
and Orion lapses into a blue funk, wondering how he offended the poor animal."

Wales sighed. "Ament's won't seem the same after you
leave."

"What eats me is that I've been working two years just
to make old Ament pay me hard wages."

"Your going to work for Orion will sure bring the old
lady back into her glory," Wales moaned. "We'll be drinking our coffee without any sugar."

Pet tugged at his goatee, offered Sam the solace of a Cuba
six, lit the cheroot for him and asked, "Is Orion going to
pay you?"

"He says three-fifty a week, but I don't see why he doesn't
make it ten, since he'll be forever owing it to me."

Pet nodded sagely. "I've got friends in the printing business, Sam. You know what they call Orion?"

"You can't make me feel any worse, so tell me."

"Well," Pet said, "their name for him is 'Parson Snivel.'

You see, up there in St. Loo, Orion took to religion like it was strawberry jam and had to be spread on everybody's bread. That wasn't so bad—underneath, everybody knows religion is good for them—but then Orion dove into the temperance swim and even went wading after the beer drinkers!"

"You should talk," Sam growled. "An old fraud of a temperance prattler like you."

But Wales chipped in his two cents' worth. "You miss the point, Sam. Pet only tells those people what they *want* to hear. He doesn't try to *change* them."

Sam dropped an argument he couldn't win. Anyhow, there was a silver lining to even this dark cloud. "You ought to see the apprentice Orion's hired—a nice, shy, empty-headed country bumpkin named Jim Wolfe."

"I guess we taught you how to handle that kind," Pet bragged.

Sam grinned. "I'll do better," he promised. "A lot better!"

Meanwhile Orion struggled to feel comfortable on the horns of the dilemma where Ma and Pamela had hung him. He launched a new weekly called the *Western Union*, then bought out another paper so that he was publishing the *Hannibal Western Union and Journal*, which was enough of a name, Sam declared, to choke anything but a cow. Apparently this opinion carried down into the meadows, for one night the cows broke into the Clemens shop, knocked over all the forms ready for the press, and chewed up two of the rollers. Orion ought to take out a patent on his kind of hard luck, Sam told Henry.

Orion couldn't keep anything secret, including his innermost feelings. Since there was no question where Ma and Pamela stood on the matter of the newspaper, and Henry didn't seem good for much of anything except pulling the dirtiest proofs this side of the devil's own print shop, it was

Sam who did the most listening while Orion bared his soul.

"Nobody ever thinks about me," Orion grumbled. "I'd still be a lawyer if I could manage it."

"Maybe you'll starve slower this way," Sam said, deciding that poor, good-hearted Orion deserved a little comfort.

"Ma thinks we'll all be rich. We never will, and that Tennessee land'll never bring a plug nickel. Now Pamela's got a fellow and talks of getting married and going to Niagara Falls on her honeymoon."

"She'll leave the piano behind. You can give music lessons on the side."

"I can't read a note," Orion said soberly, as though Sam didn't know. "And I'm not against Pamela marrying. She's twenty-two, and this chance is sink or swim with her. But here I am, doing what Ma wants and Pamela wanted, and there's nothing I'd rather do than get away from this office and fill my lungs with fresh air!"

Sam knew then that he genuinely liked Orion—he was a dash-dang fool, but Sam liked him anyhow. The fire that had burned Joan of Arc at the stake had been a lot quicker than the humdrum, everyday adversity that was consuming Orion. Yet Orion was such a confounded mixture of contradictions that Sam sometimes chewed his tongue in silent anger. Sam still nourished a hearty dislike for Benjamin Franklin, convinced that the old Philadelphia busybody had been dead-set against boys. But since Orion still clung to bossy Ben for an idol, at least he might remember, Sam thought, that no more practical man had ever lived in America.

On this score, Orion was impossible. He kept accounts as though they were bad gambling debts he'd like to forget, which, in no small measure, they were. He frittered away time writing to Ralph Waldo Emerson and Oliver Wendell Holmes, trying to get them to write original articles for the *Journal*. He extolled to them the virtues of being read in Hannibal now that its population had leaped to 2,500 (Sam knew the census figure was unreliable since he had been counted twice, once for living with Ma and once for boarding with the Aments), offered the snooty literary Yankees five dollars a piece for contributions, and sulked when they didn't even answer his letters. At the same time Orion filled long columns of the *Journal* with a story called *Bleak House*, written by an Englishman named Charles Dickens, who Sam tried to tell him was dull as dishwater. Subscriptions to Orion's paper were invariably paid for in cabbages, parsnips, and cordwood. Sam looked over the vegetables and advised his brother, "I'd burn them and eat the cordwood."

"You mind your own business," Orion retorted gruffly, overwhelmed by all his burdens.

Sam realized that Orion was keyed up and shrugged off his sass. But Henry was another problem. Sam hadn't the least notion of what heaven had decided Henry should be, but it certainly wasn't a printer. The younger boy dropped more type than three journeymen could set; he couldn't spell and wouldn't learn; and he marked a proof so that it looked as though a chicken had dipped its feet in ink and then walked over the galley. "Anyone would think you were Pet McMurray working for old Ament, the way you loaf on the job," Sam blazed at Henry.

"Sammy, I'm doin' my best."

"Your best at what—killing me by making me do your work and mine too?" Sam took the Cuba six out of his mouth and wagged it menacingly at Henry. "I'd burn your eyes out if it wasn't wasting a good cigar!"

"Ma lets you smoke, but she won't let me!"

"You get this galley corrected," Sam thundered, "or I'll smoke you, right in a barrel of tar!"

In the end, Henry's corrections only improved on the mistakes. Sam ground his teeth, lit the lamps, and turned wearily to resetting the galley. Gone were the sweet, easy, carefree days at Ament's when he could sing "Annie Laurie" or "Along the Beach at Rockaway" while he banged off handbills on the job press. Now, he simply worked and ached and ached and worked for the three-fifty a week Orion never paid him. Yet Sam had his stubborn streak. He wanted to see the *Journal* succeed and become the best rag fed on cabbages and parsnips east or west of the Mississippi. And he wanted to do it for Orion because, underneath, that fathead claimed good qualities to compensate for his lack of sense. Only—

"Faithful and industrious and upright," Sam murmured, remembering his pledge to Ma. "I only bargained to be good, not a saint!" Henry slept. Orion was off somewhere, probably eating one of the free meals he got in exchange for advertising space. Sam's eyes drooped in the flickering light.

Toward midnight Orion returned to the shop. He saw the pile of unfinished work. He saw Sam asleep. "Sam!" he cried. Halfway through tongue-lashing his brother, Orion stopped, faced with an emergency he had never before encountered. Tired Sam simply put his head on his arms and cried. He didn't care whether Orion liked it or not, he had tried just as hard as he knew how, and now he was done in. He wept quietly, forlornly, sick of everything —the *Journal*, Ma's dreams, Orion's stupidity, Henry's carelessness. "Sam!" Orion said, aghast. "I'm too hard on you. I'm a fool. Forgive me."

"Get out'n here," Sam sobbed.

So Orion left. He walked the silent streets of Hannibal. He cried all by himself. He wished the cows would come back and chew up the whole rotten paper.

Meanwhile Sam dried his eyes and finished the work.

But Sam had his fun, too. The shy country bumpkin Jim Wolfe was always around, needing his apprentice's sails trimmed, and Sam rose courageously to that responsibility. Jim had a fair complexion, a fuzz like a peach on his face, trusting brown eyes, and absolutely no imagination. Oh, you sweet one, you! Sam thought. The repertoire of bedevilment indulged in by Pet and Wales had ended with type lice and strap oil, certainly not sufficient fare to satisfy Sam's appetite. Neither Pet nor Wales would have thought of enticing a printer's devil out in a canoe, then dumping him into the old Mississippi. Luckily, Jim grabbed the end of the tipped-over craft.

"I can't swim," he wailed at Sam.

"Then float."

"I can't float."

"Then make your peace with the Lord."

"Sam," blubbered Jim, "save me, save me!"

The apprentice thrashed wildly with his legs, turning red in the face, as Sam calculated the point at which Jim was likely to burst all his veins. Then he said with disgust, "Stand up, you fool. You ain't in over your head, if you'd take the trouble to find out."

Jim finally managed to get his feet on the bottom, and to Sam's surprise the water came to the other boy's chin. "Shucks," Sam said, brightening, "guess I forgot you'd also sink a foot in this river mud!"

Next, Sam discovered that Jim's shyness extended particularly to girls. Moreover, Sam hadn't printed poems on bits of silk at Ament's without acquiring a sizable coterie of female friends. On Saturdays Jim made the composition rollers for the press, building a fire in the Clemens backyard and stewing the odoriferous concoction in a big kettle.

Sam saw the gorgeous possibilities and appeared one Saturday morning with three girls.

"Howdy, Jim," Sam called. "You cookin' a polecat?"

"You know what I'm doin'."

"Jim, if I knew, I wouldn't ask. Heat must be terrific, the way your face is turnin' red as a beet."

"It's tol'rable warm."

"Jim, don't you know cookin's of natural interest to girls? You ought to tell 'em what you've got in that pot that gives off such a good spicy smell."

"You know it's rollers," Jim grated, blushing up to the roots of his hair and down to the roots of his toenails.

"Sammy, what are rollers?" Laura Hawkins asked.

"Sort of like crullers, I guess."

"You know they're not," Jim shouted in an agony of mounting embarrassment. "They go on a press."

"That's when you put the jelly in," Sam explained quickly. "You *press* it in."

The girls, conspirators from the start in Sam's prank, began to giggle. Jim's misery rode like the horseman of death across his face. He twisted and smiled in a silly, oafish way, wiped his perspiring brow on his sleeve, and prayed that the Lord would strike him dead. Sam thought this was better sport than tipping a canoe, but Laura Hawkins, touched by the other boy's suffering, said, "Come along, Sam, and let poor Jim finish his work."

Jim shared the bedroom with Sam. All day he brooded over the terrifying indignity he had suffered. When Sam breezed into the room, Jim spoke only one word. "There!" he muttered, letting his fist fly. He caught Sam in the stomach and doubled him up on the bed. Then Jim stomped out of the room.

Sam gasped till his breath returned. "In time," he mumbled, "I'll give you tit for tat."

But even Sam could never have planned the coup that followed. One winter evening Pamela invited a group of girls to the house to make candy. Up in the bedroom Sam and Jim heard the girls run out occasionally to set their taffy under the arbor to cool. After a time all of the girls came out, laughing and trying their candy. At that moment, two mangy cats, hidden in the dead vines of the arbor where it abutted the snow-covered roof of the shed, started a woeful duet. With Jim's shyness there was also a broad streak of gallantry. "For two cents," he said, "I'd go out and knock their heads off."

Sam was enthralled at the prospective spectacle of this Sir Galahad clad only in a nightshirt. "You wouldn't dare," he goaded Jim.

"Oh, wouldn't I?" sneered Jim, snapping at the bait. He pulled on a pair of yarn stockings, threw up the sash, and balanced himself perilously on the snowy roof. Sam's eyes missed nothing—the nightshirt flapping in the breeze around Jim's legs, the crust on the snow, the spot of ice near the ledge. Nor did Sam's ear miss the continuing laughter of the girls, gathered unsuspectingly below. Jim seized a piece of lath to strike at the cats.

"You're making it, boy," Sam coached, as Jim's stock-inged feet inched closer to the ice. "Just a step or two more."

Two steps were quite enough. Jim's foot struck the ice. Up in the air shot Sir Galahad. Up in the air shot his nightshirt. Somehow the painfully modest Jim grabbed the garment and held it around his legs as he and the cats crashed through the arbor. Girls screamed. Cats, candy, fe-males, and Sir Galahad spattered, scattered, and shattered. Sam could just see all those furiously burning blushes on the faces of Sir Galahad and his candy-pulling maids in waiting. When a mortified Jim sneaked back into the room, Sam had laughed so hard he was wiping the tears from his

eyes. "You sure got rid of those cats," he shouted, throwing himself on the bed in another spasm of laughter.

In the strange way that destiny works, Jim probably had been guided to Hannibal to help lead Sam toward his intended path to eternity. So, too, must have been destiny's work the three fires that at one time or another broke out in the shop of the luckless Orion. During the second fire—the one in which Hannibal's new fire engine, the Big Mo, had been parked where nobody could find it—Jim managed to save his own peculiar assortment of valuables. The story appealed to Sam, who thought he ought to write it down. He did write it down, and Orion published it in the next issue of the *Journal*.

Our gallant *devil*, seeing us somewhat excited, concluded he would perform a noble deed, and immediately gathered the broom, an old mallet, the washpan and a dirty towel, and in a fit of patriotic excitement, rushed out of the office and deposited his precious burden some ten squares off, out of danger. Being of *snailish* disposition, even in his quickest moments, the fire had been extinguished during his absence. He returned in the course of an hour, nearly out of breath, and thinking he had immortalized himself, threw his giant frame in a tragic attitude, and exclaimed, with an eloquent expression: "If that thar fire hadn't bin put out, thar'd a'bin the greatest *confirmation* of the age!"

Even Orion chuckled. "So Jim thinks a conflagration is a confirmation?"

"I reckon."

"Sam, it's good copy." And then Orion had to be himself. "A bit hard on Jim, ridiculing him in public, but then he'll know you didn't mean it that way." Orion thought, too, a little lecture was long overdue, so he added, "Sammy, you have to be careful with a pen. It can cut a person deeper than a knife."

"Amen, Parson Snivel," Sam said to himself.

After the fire the writing bug nibbled insistently at Sam. He could now see why Orion's paper was muddling along, not worth more than parsnips and cabbages. Who wanted to read that endless story by that deadhead Dickens? Orion never killed an advertisement, even when nobody paid for it any longer, since it filled space. The *Journal* lacked humor, local interest, vitality. All at once luck played into Sam's hands. Orion was forced to be away on business for over a week, and Sam had the chance to publish the paper *his* way.

13.

Cub Editor

SAM THREW his whole heart into the venture. He loved fun, and now he intended to have it. Unlike Orion, he was not troubled with qualms about how deeply his pen might cut, and he nourished one or two grudges that he believed he could work off. Arriving at the print shop early that first day, Sam spread out paper, quill, and ink with the disorderliness of the seasoned editor. His mind recaptured the image of Joseph Ament and he thought vindictively: That runty old scoundrel never did give me the other suit of clothes he promised! Then with a chuckle more malicious than mirthful, Sam reached for the pen and began to chronicle for the amusement of the readers of the *Journal* certain revealing events that had happened during a recent exhibit when the stage curtain had caught on fire.

The source of his story, Sam wrote, was "a youngster"— meaning himself. Since Ament was a Democrat, and Pierce and King were the leading Democratic candidates in the forthcoming elections, Sam's fertile imagination quickly identified Ament as a member of the audience. "Now it is well known that the editor of the ———— is a very quiet, well behaved little fellow, and sits still, like a good boy, as he is, unless some unlooked for accident occurs, or Pierce and

King are mentioned." Sam's chuckle deepened. Everyone knew that Ament's print shop was directly across the street from the hall where the curtain had caught fire. Joyfully Sam's pen scratched on, " 'Thar he sot,' pale as a sheet, shaking like double rectified ague; his eyes standing out from his head; his 'nail-grabs' grasping a pew like grim death." In a triumph of invective Sam laced away at "this soft-soaper of Democratic rascality . . . this father of nothing," who in ridiculously needless alarm jumped over nine pews and dashed from the hall!

"Pet and Wales will adore that," Sam told himself hilariously. "And the old woman will get so excited she'll dump the whole bowl of sugar into their coffee!"

Henry, reading the story, was dubious. "Sammy, old Ament will horsewhip you for this!"

"He hasn't the strength."

"Then he'll get his lackeys, Pet an' Wales, to do it for him."

"They haven't the ambition."

"Maybe *she'll* take a shotgun to you," Henry said.

Sam arched an eyebrow. "I'll watch her," he promised. "Now lookit here, young sport, you hustle that copy into type."

Henry still balked. "Shucks, Sam, we've got enough old ads and filler around the place to make up a paper till Orion gets back. He ain't goin' to like this kind of story, anyhow."

"Orion!" shouted Sam, bouncing up from the chair. "What does he know 'bout what people want to read? I'll dock your wages if you ain't quick getting that story in type!"

Henry shrugged. "Who pays me?" But when Sam snatched for the mallet on the composing table, Henry fled to the type cases.

When Sam had produced his next literary effort, back to the editor's desk came Henry, full of complaints. "Sammy, who in blazes is W. Epaminondas Adrastus Blab?"

"That's me. That's my pen name. It's a whistler!"

"It's too long. It'd be easier to set shortened to Blab."

Sam reckoned that no budding young genius ever had labored under more trying circumstances. He flung down his pen and clamped a Cuba six in his mouth. Then he picked up a stove poker with a hook on the end in case Henry had any notion of ducking out before he finished speaking his mind. "Now lookit here, young sport," he said, "this whole bloomin' paper is so dull even Ma can't stand to read Orion's editorials any longer. The *Journal* is goin' downhill so fast the farmers put false bottoms in the baskets when they bring in their spoiled vegetables to pay for their subscriptions. I wouldn't be surprised if we were carrying the advertisement of an undertaker who died three years ago. Pretty soon everything'll go bust if something doesn't wake this town up to the fact that the *Journal* exists. I'm going to do it, and you're going to help me, or by Godfrey and by gadfly I'll wring your neck an' poke out your eyes an' grind up your carcass into sausage meat!"

Henry nodded and gulped. "Sam, words come out of you like water out'n a pump!"

"And the wrath comes out of me like out'n Jehovah," mimicked Sam, but underneath he wanted to grin. Henry had a sparkle that poor old Orion would never possess. As mongrel pups went, Henry was almost endurable.

Actually, Sam's compositions under the pseudonym of W. Epaminondas Adrastus Blab appealed to Henry. The first was entitled "Historical Exhibition—A No. 1 Ruse," and dealt with a hoax played by a venerable Hannibal citizen upon a Jim C—— and his friends. The old-timer had charged the gullible Jim and his cronies a fee to see "Bonaparte Crossing the Rhine," Sam claimed, but his exhibition had consisted of no more than a bone laid across a strip of bacon rind. Another outpouring, labeled "Blabbing Government Secrets," professed that a special session of the Missouri legislature had been called to abbreviate the writer's name to "Blab," and "all at a cost of only a few thousands of dollars to the State."

No matter what Orion might think, Sam was having the time of his life. He read Hannibal's rival weeklies more diligently than Orion, and had followed in one of them an inane controversy over a law requiring all dogs to be licensed at a dollar a head. The editor of the *Messenger* had started this wrangle, remaining excited about a mad-dog scare through five consecutive issues, and a correspondent to Orion's paper, signing himself "A Dog-be-Deviled Citizen," had called for the extermination of all dogs.

Sam's talents were drawn to this issue as though it contained something magnetic. Since he had disposed of one rival editor in his satire about Ament, he saw no reason for sparing the sensibilities of his other competitor. "A new broom sweeps clean," hummed Sam, hoping, for Orion's sake, that he quoted from that sanctimonious old fogy Franklin. Sam had never lacked a nose for news. The editor of the *Messenger*, local rumor insisted, had been jilted in love and was said to have gone to the river one night to commit suicide.

Sam's eyes sparkled. He would do better than concoct this story, he would illustrate it. Using the reverse side of a block of wooden type, Sam cut with a jackknife the picture of a dog-headed man employing a cane to ascertain the depth of the water. Gaily, Sam wrote:

"Local" Resolves to Commit Suicide

'LOCAL,' disconsolate from receiving no further notice from 'A DOG-BE-DEVILED CITIZEN' contemplates suicide. His 'pocket pistol' (i.e. the *bottle*,) failing in the patriotic work of ridding the country of a nuisance, he resolves to 'extinguish his chunk' by feeding his carcass to the fishes of Bear Creek, while friend and foe are wrapt in sleep. Fearing, however, that he may get out of his depth, he *sounds the stream with his walking-stick.*

The artist has, you will perceive, Mr. Editor, caught the gentleman's countenance as correctly as the thing could have been done with the real *dog*gerytype apparatus. Ain't he pretty? and don't he step along through the mud with an air? 'Peace to his *re*-manes.'

'A DOG-BE-DEVILED CITIZEN.'

Henry shook his head. "You think you dare run this, Sam?"

"Of course I dare! Piffle to the editor of the *Messenger!* People who say they're going to commit suicide knowing they'd holler bloody murder if anybody pushed 'em into a foot of water deserve to be exposed as lily-livered braggarts! I say, let the press run! As the Californy gold rushers would declare, the *Journal*'ll wake 'em up or bust a-tryin'!"

Henry glanced over Sam's shoulder at another sheet of paper on the desk. "Is that something else to go in?"

"No, Henry—that's an idea for next summer."

"Next summer!" Henry exclaimed. "Do you think you'll live that long after Orion sees what you've done?" But Henry's eyes couldn't resist glancing at the writing—already Sam had won him as a steady reader—and then the younger brother began to giggle. Sam had scribbled:

To prevent Dogs going mad in August:
Cut their heads off in July.

"Sammy, I guess it's so," Henry said. "If Orion'd let you run this paper all the time, the *Journal* would get somewheres!"

"We'll soon find out," laughed an exuberant Sam. "Roll the press!"

The press rumbled steadily that day—and the next and

the next. All at once the *Journal* was in demand. People even paid cash to get copies. Pet and Wales whispered to Sam that old Ament was sharpening a hatchet—he wasn't going to use it on Sam, but the old lady expected to. The editor of the *Messenger* was undecided between two courses—to tar and feather Sam or to sneak out of town. He chose the latter. Sam glowed with pride when he saw loungers in the tavern chuckling over the *Journal* and pointing out to friends what they had been reading. His heart thumped merrily. Sooner or later he would have to deal with Orion, but until the time came he intended to walk blissfully along his rosy path of triumph.

Orion, returning, hadn't the imagination to guess that his paper might be on the brink of success. Through humorless eyes he read Sam's compositions with a shocked and sinking heart. "I'm breaking you, Sammy," he said bitterly. "You're reduced to the same status as Henry."

"You mean, I don't get paid my wages either?" Sam flung back, burningly sarcastic.

Orion's hackles rose. "You know how hard times are—Ma taking in boarders, Pamela marrying and off living in St. Louis, eggs twenty cents a dozen, wood at four dollars a cord. And now you try to make a joke book out of the *Journal*—it's not right!"

"Some day," Sam said softly, "if you ever want to write your life story, I've got the perfect title. Call it *The Autobiography of a Damned Fool.*"

Orion stared hard, and one of the reasons why it was difficult to tell how his mind worked was the fact that when one day he did write his life story, he used the very title Sam suggested. Now he said, deciding that he didn't want their wrangle to grow any nastier, "I know you're young, Sammy, and have your heart in the right place. Somehow we'll fix it up."

"Fixing up," under Orion's direction, consisted first of an obituary written by Sam for the next issue:

FOR THE JOURNAL.

Mr. Editor:

I believe it is customary, nowadays, for a man, as soon as he gets his name up, to take a "furrin" tour, for the benefit of his health; or, if his health is good, he goes without any excuse at all. Now, I think my health was sufficiently injured by last week's efforts, to justify me in starting on my tour; and, ere your hebdomadal is published, I shall be on my way to another country—yes, Mr. Editor, I have retired from public life to the shades of Glasscock's Island [where Sam and Tom had often played]—and I shall gratify such of your readers as have never been so far from home, with an account of this great island, and my voyage thither.

W. EPAMINONDAS ADRASTUS BLAB.

Orion permitted the dog controversy to continue temporarily—Sam had already cut two more pictures, and by nature Orion could stand to waste nothing—but then an editorial note written by Orion informed the readers of the *Journal* that he had found the subject a bore and was dropping it.

Unable ever to nurse a grudge, Orion shortly relented and permitted Sam to write articles of which he approved. But Sam still worked late hours, doing his work and much of Henry's. He felt keenly his personal impoverishment and wished that even if butter was twenty cents a pound, Orion would pay him something on almost six years of back wages. Sam was more sensitive than Orion to the growing strain between them. In a sly poke at the older brother, one of Sam's quips in the *Journal* punned, "Well, we are all subject to change, except printers; they never have any spare *change*."

14.

A Widening Rift

SAM NOW APPROACHED his eighteenth year. He had not grown into an Adonis, but he thought his face was tol'-rable. He was obviously strong, for he was performing the work of six mules. Ordinarily he was pleasant and good-humored, and his friends seemed to like listening to his slow drawl when he told a story. Jimmy McDaniel had fallen off a log and nearly knocked out his brains at Sam's account of how Jim Wolfe, in his nightshirt, had fallen through the arbor during the candy pull.

Yet Sam recognized that something was deeply, disturbingly wrong. He was standing on his own feet, and yet, in a way, he wasn't. He was in a rut, toiling like a slave and feeling almost as penniless, as trapped. He wasn't free, so what self-respect could he have? If it weren't for Orion and the paper, could he still get along? Would anybody else ever need him, or want him? He heard an echo from the past, and in memory he was back with Tom and Bence, sitting on an island deep in the Illinois bottoms and hearing a Negro say, "Ah reckon Ah did it from thinkin' 'bout how a bird jus' born learns to fly off by hisself, an' how an ole wolf train her cub so he kin do his own chicken-stealin', an' how white chillun growed up an' say good-by to dere folks an' strike out on dere own. Dat's how God planned de world. Every creature was to have his chance to be free, an' see how he kin make out by hisself, an' laugh at hisself fo' bein' a fool or give hisself a pat on de back an' say, 'Boy, you ain't so bad, considerin'.' You see how it is?"

Yes, more than ever, Sam saw how it was. His normal disposition cried out at too long stretches of moodiness. He shook off his glumness, and then turned a corner and unexpectedly everything came back—his unrest, his sense of forlornness and futility and fretfulness.

In one of Sam's most depressed spells, a January evening in 1853, he walked the streets of Hannibal, trying to make up his mind what to do, where to go. Crossing Wildcat Corner he heard raucous, taunting laughter down by the river. Lanky strides carried Sam to the noise, and he beheld poor Dennis McDermid surrounded by a throng of children.

Dennis was a doddering harmless old tramp, and the temperance people never gave a lecture without a dozen or more references to Dennis as a sublime example of what drinking could do to a man. Hannibal children, working off their savage impulses, also looked upon Dennis as their personal property. Sam found them now, dancing around the poor tramp and shrilling raucously, "Dennis, Dennis—needs repentance!"

"Crazy Dennis, crazy Dennis!"

The old fellow tried to appear unconcerned, so the children danced closer and screamed louder.

"Drunk old Dennis! Drunk old Dennis!"

"You can't catch me, Dennis! Tag—you're it, Dennis!" A small boy, darting closer, collided with the man's legs and sent him stumbling and reeling. Then a larger boy, about ten or eleven, picked up a clod of dirt.

"Don't throw that!" Sam shouted. The older boy took

no heed. The clod of dirt flew through the air and struck
the back of Dennis' neck. The impact of the blow sent the
man sprawling in a heap.

The tormenting chorus rose hysterically.

"Dennis, Dennis! Chase us, chase us!"

One little girl singsonged brazenly, "Drunk old Dennis
down in the road, a-makin' love to a cross-eyed toad!"

Sam could endure no more. He charged into the circle,
clapping his hand over the girl's mouth and hissing, "Get
home to your Ma before I hang you to a tree by your pigtails!" The boy who had thrown the clod jumped a foot
when Sam booted his bottom. "Get away from Dennis!"
roared an infuriated Sam, and frightened children appeared
to melt into the shadows along the river. Gently, Sam helped
Dennis back to his feet.

"They don't mean it bad, Sam," old Dennis said.

On the point of telling Dennis not to be a sentimental
slob, Sam caught himself. He remembered Bence, who at
one time would have danced with those jeering young
hoodlums and yet, over in the Illinois bottoms, had set the
toy canoe adrift. "What can I do for you, Dennis?" Sam
asked warmly.

"You got a match for an old man's pipe?"

Sam struck a match and held it to Dennis' blackened
corncob. The old fellow sucked, but accidentally blew out
the match. Still wobbling from his fall, he took the pipe
from his mouth and said contritely, "I'm right sorry to
pester you this way, Sam."

"Let's try again." But now Dennis dropped his pipe, and
Sam not only retrieved it, but also lighted the tobacco.
"There, Dennis, puff on that."

"Bless you, Sam."

"And here's a handful of matches for later."

"You're a good lad."

Sam still didn't want to leave the poor tramp alone. "Where will you sleep tonight?"

"Oh, don't trouble your head about that," Dennis cackled. "Hannibal's a good town. It looks out for its own. Pretty soon the marshall'll be along an' throw old Dennis in the calaboose. Me, I'll have a snug, warm straw bed tonight. So don't you worry your head, Sammy. I'll get along fine!"

Sam walked home, thinking that for all the world's cruel knocks, most people were wonderfully brave and decent, even a Dennis McDermid. In the human heart there seemed to be a place for almost everyone. Except the deliberate, brutal bully, Sam's mind appended. In a lifetime, Sam thought, you might find a few blackguards who tried to trap and enslave and rule and cripple the hopes and dreams of others. Those he could despise with a passion, and go after them with a will to beat down the tyrants and cheats, the persecutors of his Joan of Arc.

"Sam Clemens," the humorous side of him said, "go home and get in bed before you begin to weep and flood the Mississippi clear down to Memphis!"

In cheerful spirits Sam retired, grateful to Dennis for the lift he had given him. Sometime after midnight the church bells began to toll, and Sam bolted out of bed. Fire! He dressed hastily and fled into the street.

For weeks, for months, the scene he encountered remained a raw, bleeding memory—the calaboose in flames, Dennis' pale face pressed against the bars of the window, and in the sky the smoke, the stars, the placid moon. In his ears Sam heard over and over the screams of agony, of terror, of blind and uncontrollable animal suffering—the stark, terrible requiem of a person being burned alive.

And through it all, Sam felt that he *knew*. Dazed, he walked along the dark river. He had given Dennis the matches. When the poor fellow had tried to light his pipe, he must have dropped the burning match, and around him the straw of his bed must have leaped into a roaring inferno!

"Oh, God! Oh, God!" Sam moaned wretchedly. "I'm responsible for the death of Dennis McDermid! I'm responsible for taking the life of a human being!"

All, from a handful of matches! The terrible conviction of guilt grew in Sam's heart, constricting it, seizing him in a dry, secret grief that would not yield to the comfort of shameless tears.

Below him the dark water gurgled and groaned, and he saw dimly an old sycamore that leaned perilously, for the Mississippi had seeped under its roots and slowly, but stubbornly, was drawing the tree to its death in the mud of the river. He shuddered visibly, sensing this symbol of the world's brutality—man destroyed by man, a tree by nature. Across his mind flashed the image of Injun Joe in his red wig, a living corpse. He wanted suddenly to leave Hannibal, to wander to far distances, to break free from this place where now, his conscience told him, he would forever see in his dreams the pale face of Dennis McDermid pressed against the barred window of the burning cell.

For days Sam could neither eat nor sleep. Ma, Henry, no one seemed capable of reaching him, consoling him. Orion couldn't print the story of Dennis' death without drawing a moral: "Even he might have found a better friend than whisky." Sam flung the paper aside, disgusted. He could see clearly now how the rift between Orion and himself was destined to grow ever wider. Orion harped on the evil of *drinking* and never saw that the real tragedy was in *wanting* to drink, in feeling that life was so dead set against you that you had to drink. Orion would bind his fellow men with pledges, and Sam would free them to face the world unafraid.

One day Ma called sharply, "Sam!" He stopped in the door,

hangdoggish. "You're breaking your heart and mine, too. And it's stupid, Sam Clemens. You didn't kill Dennis Mc-Dermid any more than the jailer who didn't get there in time with the key, or the firemen who didn't put out the fire."

Sam said, "Ma, I feel so rotten!"

And Jane Clemens answered, "Well, you big over-sensitive fool, you've taught me one thing these past three months. I'd still love you if you had killed a man."

"Ma, you know I couldn't—not meaning to."

"That I've always known, Sammy."

"All my life, you've been good to me."

Jane Clemens smiled and wiped away a tear and said, "You see why I could always share Pa's dream about the Tennessee land? It's because it was part of the other dream we shared—for you and Henry and Orion and Pamela and the poor, sweet children who died. I'm not much on kissing, Sammy, but I wish you'd kiss me now."

Sam did.

For Ma's sake, Sam tried to drift along with Orion and patch up the rift that nature appeared to be forcing between them. Night after night Sam worked late, carrying the work of two on the wages of none, and Orion understood and encouraged Sam to write more for the paper. So new pen names appeared in the *Journal*—"Rambler" and "Grumbler" —and when Sam wrote jibes that made him wince, Orion kept his disapproval to himself. Sammy was just odd, Orion guessed. He had to defend any underdog from town drunks to runaway slaves, and he laughed at people who wrote sentimental poetry, a rage in Hannibal during 1853. With fingers crossed, Orion went off in May on another business trip, leaving his problem brother in charge of the print shop.

Sam romped all over the next issue of the *Journal*. One of the inspirations that tickled him was a startling hoax.

Terrible Accident
500 Men Killed and Missing ! ! !

We had set the above head up, expecting (of course) to use it, but as the accident hasn't happened, yet, we'll say (To be Continued.)

For Hannibal's tribe of mushy poets, who Sam swore drove him out of his mind with their asinine verses, he contrived his own lovesick ballad, and then, laughing himself into a weak-kneed ecstasy, appended the title.

To Miss Katie in H------L

A shrieking Henry spluttered, "Poor Orion, wait till he sees this sensation!" and went into another gleeful spree of rolling on the floor.

"Let those who don't believe H------L stands for Hannibal be responsible for their own wicked thoughts," hooted Sam.

Orion returned, baffled (again his circulation had increased), hurt (for Sam after all should remember that the *Journal* appeared under the name of Orion Clemens, Publisher), and too harried with mortgage payments and other financial worries to make a scene. When the break came, it was precipitated by an apparently trivial incident.

"Orion," Sam said one day, "I want some money."

"What for?"

"Because you owe it to me—for almost six years—fifty-two times three dollars and a half, times six!"

"Ask for compound interest while you're at it, Sammy," Orion said wryly. "I haven't any chance of paying that either."

Sam grinned. "I know. And I'm not really complaining. All I want is ten dollars."

Again Orion asked guardedly, "What for?"

"To buy a gun."

Orion flared up. "Who can eat a gun? Haven't you any sense, Sam? I've got to think of Ma and Henry as well as you and me. What little cash I get goes to put food on the table."

"Food!" roared Sam. "Week after week of bacon, butter, bread, and coffee—you call that eating, you confounded, short-sighted, pigeon-brained, cold-water crusader!"

"You're not starving!"

"Do I get the ten dollars for the gun?"

"No!"

Sam ripped off his printer's apron and flung it on Orion's desk. "Then I'm through," he shouted, and stomped out of the print shop.

In misery Jane Clemens helped him pack. "Where are you going, Sammy?"

"To St. Louis. To see Pamela and her husband."

He knew he lied. But how could he tell Ma that he had been reading about the Crystal Palace Fair in New York City and yearned to visit it? Right in Orion's paper Ma could read how in the fleshpot of New York "drunkenness and debauching are carried on to their fullest extent."

Jane Clemens straightened up. "I suppose, Sammy, what most of all you've got to find is yourself."

"What I mean—to the world," he interjected.

Ma went to the dresser and took down her Bible.

"Sammy," she said, "I want you to repeat these words after me: 'I do solemnly swear that I will not throw a card or drink a drop of liquor while I am gone.' "

"Ma, I give you my promise."

At the door, Jane Clemens held out her hand to him and asked in a choked voice, "Would you promise me one thing more, Sammy?"

"What's that, Ma?"

"Write to me now and then."

He nodded. He couldn't trust himself to speak. He caught the night boat for St. Louis, never dreaming that a distracted Orion almost sobbed to Ma, "Well, he's gone—because I was gloomy, taciturn, and selfish!"

From the deck of the river boat Sam stared down at the Hannibal dock, fast fading into the darkness. Now old John Hannicks could feed his sway-backed horse and go to bed. And Pet McMurray could smoke a Cuba six in memory of him, and Henry had dash-dang better learn how to spell at last. And they needn't think he wouldn't miss them—all of them, even old lunkhead Orion—because he was bawling right now. But he had to go. He had to find out for himself. He had to be free because if he wasn't, he would be better off caught under the roots of a tree in the Illinois bottoms.

He couldn't say good-by. Not to Hannibal. Maybe he'd never see this old hog-drovers' paradise again, yet it would always remain in his heart, a clear and shining sacred memory.

Then, his irrepressible sense of humor playing tricks on him, he chuckled as he saw the dandy banner Orion should publish in next week's *Journal*.

SAM CLEMENS LEAVES H———L.

15.

The Wanderer

SAM LINGERED in St. Louis two months while a job as typesetter on the *Evening Post* supplied the money to carry him to the magic of the Crystal Palace Fair in New York City. Then for five days he jiggled and jolted, moaned and groaned and slept not a wink, growled that he ate cinders for breakfast, lunch, and supper and wondered why he ate at all since his insides had been joggled out during the first day of a bouncing train trip across Illinois and Michigan, a rolling steamer voyage across Lake Erie, a rail trip behind a veteran smoke snorter from Buffalo to Albany, and a sail down the Hudson River in an old tub left over from Noah's boatyard. Through all five days, mouth grimly clamped on a cigar that he could keep lighted only in those intervals when passengers were not crawling over his lap, or children were not using the back of his neck for a spitball target, or bundles were not falling out of the rack and making colored constellations explode in his head, Sam wrangled with the problem of explaining to Ma why he was no longer in St. Louis. The sly approach he concocted made him grin.

My dear Mother: You will doubtless be a little surprised, and somewhat angry when you receive this, and find me so far from home; but you must bear a little with me, for you know I was always the best boy you had, and perhaps you remember that people used to say to their children—"Now don't do like O. and H.C.—but take S. for your guide!"

Well, I was out of work in St. Louis, and didn't fancy loafing in such a dry place, where there is not pleasure to be seen without paying well for it, and so I thought I might as well go to New York. I packed my "duds" and left for this village, where I arrived, all right, this morning.

O Sammy, you artful purveyor of woeful lies! his conscience nagged. But then he chuckled. He was in New York with three dollars in his pocket, ten dollars sewn into the lining of his coat, and ten thousand dollars worth of hope in his heart!

Sam's luck proved far better than he deserved. Cool weather also had arrived, sweeping from the city a long spell of muggy, scalding August days that had left tongues extended and tempers contracted. A yellow-fever epidemic had driven many Southerners north, and for every opening in the printing offices there were ten applicants. Yet Sam, a friendly, good-humored Midwestern boy who would have wagged a tail if he had possessed the luck to have been born a dog, walked into the establishment of John A. Gray, at 97 Cliff Street, and was instantly hired at four dollars a week —in wildcat money, which made it worth about three.

Sam liked Gray's at once. The composing room was on the fifth floor, one side looking over the cluttered buildings of the city and the other upon the forest of masts in the harbor where the cargo ships of the world anchored. Yet the forty compositors packed into the room were there to work and not to gaze. The foreman, a slim, soft-voiced, tigerish little fellow, decided from the start that Sam could accept him as friend or foe, but either way they were coming to terms that first day.

"You're Clemens, eh?"

"Samuel L. Clemens, sir."

"Where you from?"

"Hannibal."

"Where in Sam Hill is that?"

"In Missouri, sir. On the Mississippi."

"I've heard of the river," the foreman said, a bit grudgingly. "Some say it is bigger than the Hudson, but I don't go for such braggarts. The Hudson's a mighty pretty river, Clemens."

"It's pretty coming down from Albany."

"Better than the Rhine, some say. That's why I won't stand for you Mississippi boys running down our river."

Sam bit his tongue. He wished to run neither up nor down the river. But the foreman was simply being sociable. Now he got down to business. "You're in New York City," he said as though Sam were too stupid to know it. "You understand what that means?"

Sam groped desperately for an answer, his sweat pores beginning to open like dikes, but the foreman plunged on in a bluster. "I'll tell you what it means. Quality. Q-u-a-l-i-t-y! Everything's got to be the best, see? We try to be perfect. P-e-r-f-e-c-t, Clemens, and I'd like you to fix that in your mind first in italics and then in small caps."

Sam wanted to ask, "How many exclamation points?"

The foreman expected him to say nothing, for he went on. "No, Clemens, out in Cicero or Caesar or wherever in Sam Hill you came from, they don't know how to set type. I've seen the filth they turn out, Clemens—I tell you, it's f-i-l-t-h. One line they'll space with three em spaces and the next with five ems. Do they put the same space between every word? They do not, Clemens—they d-o n-o-t! Do they space every line exactly alike? Not those pigs-turned-printers, Clemens—and that's what they are, p-i-g-s!"

Sam almost grinned. Never had he heard the practices of

Orion's shop or Ament's so perfectly described. Meanwhile the foreman raised a finger, waved it at the cub's nose, and growled, "You've been told. This is New York where q-u-a-l-i-t-y counts. Give us your Scipio or Alexander or Mark Antony pig printing, and I tell you, Clemens, o-u-t you go!"

"Yes, sir," Sam said. He meant to make good at Gray's, his first job a thousand miles away from home, even if the foreman insisted that he set type while standing on his head. He spaced everything so evenly that he wondered if he shouldn't get a square haircut. Within a week the Mississippi boy was producing the cleanest proof at Gray's and the Hudson River man told him warmly, "We can use lads like you, Clemens. Yes, sir, that's nice work—real n-i-c-e!"

Sam glowed. He was secure in his job and he had been fortunate to find a place to board about a mile away, close enough to hear the blast of Gray's steam whistle calling the help to work each morning. Food, lodging, and laundry left him fifty cents at the end of the week. He was rich.

The steam whistle also screeched the end of the day's work at Gray's, and as Sam bolted down the five flights of stairs, his heart thumped with the anticipation of another evening of marvels at the Crystal Palace Fair. Narrow, winding Cliff Street crawled with children—Negroes, mulattoes, quadroons, Chinese, and some, Sam wrote Ma, whom "the Lord no doubt originally intended to be white, but the dirt on whose faces leaves one uncertain as to the fact."

"Out of the way, you trundle-bed trash!" bellowed Sam, eager to get to his dinner. But youngsters blocked his path. Youngsters hooted derisively into his splitting eardrums. Youngsters ran around him and against him and almost through him. "Catfish and kittens!" exploded Sam. "Don't tell me I ever belonged to such a mass of human vermin!"

Valiantly he fought his way along Cliff Street and Frankfort and Nassau until he reached Broadway, gaining an empty victory. Now, he had to buffet homeward-bound workers by wedging himself into the midst of a moving human cater-pillar, not troubling to use his own legs as he pushed and shoved and rubbed along. "It seems like I had been pulled to pieces and very badly put together again," he confessed to Ma. But supper restored his strength and courage, and off he charged to the Crystal Palace.

A letter told Pamela, " 'Tis a perfect fairy palace." Every day six thousand persons—double the population of Hannibal —passed into the magnificent structure. At fifty cents a head the daily income was three thousand dollars, enough to put Orion and the *Journal* on Easy Street for life. Local pride took Sam to the exhibit Hannibal had sent to the fair, but compared to the mechanical, botanical, and architectural wonders that had come from cities throughout the world, he couldn't say that Hannibal's bale of hemp and two bar-rels of flour was any show stopper.

Sam's love for the bizarre drew him irresistibly to the "wild men" of Borneo. He stared at the unhappy captives, shaking his head. Without Adam's apples, they could utter no sound. Phizzes, he thought, that look more orangutang than human. Their strength was tremendous, and Sam watched them handle a hundred-pound-weight more easily than he could lift a plug of tobacco. Back and forth, twenty-three hours out of twenty-four, the poor brutes tramped their cages. "When they fix their glittering orbs on you with a steady, unflinching gaze," he wrote Ma, "you instinctively draw back a step, and a very unpleasant sensation steals through your veins."

With the passing days Sam began to feel enough at home in the city to grow critical. His Southern-bred taste buds missed their hot bread, and what New Yorkers called light bread consisted of an ordinary loaf that had been allowed to turn stale. He tramped off to see Edwin Forrest in *The Gladiator* at the Broadway Theater, and in the last act when the gladiator died at his brother's feet, Sam believed that Forrest's whole soul was absorbed in the performance. Here was no Hannibal amateur lunacy, but the stage transformed into a vehicle of human emotion.

Other days sped by—out of bed at the blast of Gray's whistle, a day of typesetting under the burning eyes of the tigerish foreman, then home again through the welter of screaming children, New York's principal article of manu-

facture. In tired moments Sam often felt alone, an outsider —a Missourian on free soil, where Negroes sassed back. He lamented in a letter home the image of Uncle Dan'l in his mind, "I would like amazingly to see a good old-fashioned Negro." Underneath, he felt a sense of guilt. He had tricked Ma. He had run away—from Orion, anyhow.

"Bother with Parson Snivel," he sneered unconvincingly. Henry must have the shop in a mess by now. Yet Henry was young; no one should expect miracles. He wished he'd get a letter from Hannibal. Then he did and wished he hadn't.

Ma sent a copy of the *Journal* in which Orion had published one of the letters from New York, adding in a note,
"The free and easy impudence of the writer will be appreciated by those who recognize him." Sam winced, feeling
that from across half a continent Orion was trying to cut
him down to size. He'd like to see Orion, for all his high and
mighty airs, hold a job at Gray's! He'd like to see him have
fifty cents for himself at the end of the week! Suddenly
Sam's vindictiveness collapsed. For years Orion had held a
steady job in St. Louis, and after Pa's death he had sent Ma
three dollars every week. Orion, the plodder, had his place,
his reason for existing.

Restlessness stirred in Sam. All right, let Orion think it,
say it! He, Sam, was in New York on a skylark—the same
boyish Sammy who thought the *Journal* was a joke book!
News that Henry had been sick further disturbed Sam,
awakening him to a deepening affection for the younger
boy, and he scolded Pamela, "He ought to go to the country
and take exercise, for he is not half so healthy as Ma thinks
he is. If he had my walking to do, he would be another boy
entirely."

What he heard and saw, the pace and attitude of the city,
seemed to rip a mask from Sam's eyes, and all at once he was
appalled at how little education he actually possessed. Now,
he spent nights at the library, poring over books by the
armful, and even enjoying Orion's old standby, Charles
Dickens. He tried to fool himself into thinking he belonged
where he was, and wrote to Pamela with a note of bellig-
erency:

> If you have a brother nearly eighteen years of age who is
> not able to take care of himself a few miles from home, such
> a brother is not worth one's thoughts; and if I don't manage
> to take care of No. 1, be assured you will never know it. I
> am not afraid, however; I shall ask favors of no one and

endeavor to be (and shall be) as "independent as a wood-sawyer's clerk."

There, he had as much as said it—he was no Orion and never intended to be. But when shortly he threw up his job at Gray's he moved on to the citadel of Orion's adopted patron saint, and tumbled into a job on the *Philadelphia Inquirer* as easily as he had at Gray's. In a new world to conquer he reverted quickly to the old, carefree Sam. A compositor named Frog, who had worked at a case in the *Inquirer's* composing room so long nobody could remember when he started, flew into a tantrum if a line with a hook and a bit of red flannel on it was hung in front of him. "His Pap must have been a bull—way back, 'bout the time Aunt Nell was so chummy with Moses," gaily declared Sam, one of the most persistent practitioners of the prank. Frog was almost blind from a lifetime of typesetting, twisted like a pretzel with rheumatism; Sam's delight in Frog's irascibility demonstrated that he had not yet outgrown the trundle-bed trash.

Frog owned a house in a distant part of Philadelphia and possessed an abnormal fear of fire. Sam was soon recruiting a fellow compositor for a new prank. Waiting till there was scarcely a sound in the room except the clicking of type being set, Sam strode to the window, sniffed prodigiously, and exclaimed, "Doesn't that smoke seem to be in the northwestern part of the city?"

Up came Frog's crooked old back with a creak. The partner Sam had coached so carefully chimed in, "There goes that fire bell again!"

Frog set down his typestick. Laboriously, painfully, he climbed the steps to the roof while Sam locked arms with his crony and danced around the room. Eventually Frog returned, grumbling, "Must have been a train or a steamer on the Schuylkill. Thankee, Sammy, for warning me, though. If you smell smoke again, I'd like to know it."

In the next few weeks no one had ever smelled so much smoke as Sam. Each time, Frog, as tireless as Sam, lumbered off to the roof.

Again news from home disturbed Sam. The *Journal* had failed; Orion had sold out, settled for a time in Muscatine, Iowa, and then moved the family to Keokuk where, wonder of the century, he was courting a girl. He was starting a new establishment, which he planned to call the Ben Franklin Book and Print Shop, and Sam, with Orion on his mind, walked over to Christ Churchyard to view the old patriot's tomb. Afterward he wrote Orion:

> Unlike New York, I like this Philadelphia amazingly, and the people in it. There is only one thing gets my "dander" up—and that is the hands that are always encouraging me; telling me "it's no use to get discouraged—no use to be down-hearted, for there is more work here than you can do!" "Down-hearted," the devil! I have not had a particle of such a feeling since I left Hannibal. I fancy they'll have to wait some time till they see me down-hearted or afraid of starving while I have the strength to work and am in a city of 400,000 inhabitants. When I was in Hannibal, before I had scarcely stepped out of the town limits, nothing could have convinced me that I would starve as soon as I got a little way from home.

And that, by gadfly, was telling Orion! Unfortunately it wasn't telling Sam. January arrived, bleak and chill, and Sam began feeling the return of the old depressed spirit that had plagued him a year ago and driven him to wandering the streets of Hannibal on that ill-fated night when he had given the matches to Dennis McDermid. The novelties of Philadelphia palled, even the habit of Philadelphia women when riding on a streetcar to hand their money to strange men next to them, who in turn passed it on to the conductor —a custom that, in St. Louis, would have made any lady feel her reputation had been ruined. Sam had kept his pledge to Ma, and sometimes felt he was the only compositor on the *Inquirer* who didn't drink. At work, now and then, he found himself leaning over the type case humming "An exile from home, splendor dazzles in vain." His pranks on Frog had completely lost their savor. Poor old fellow needed a rest, anyhow.

Some evenings he tried to write. He chewed the nub of his pen, groping for a pseudonym, something with a good jingle to it like W. Epaminondas Adrastus Blab! But the name never came, and the stuff he wrote was dull and lifeless. He could almost feel Orion bending over his shoulder, watching, reading, and Sam knew he strained to please his brother rather than himself. He crumpled the paper and flung it across the room, asking bitterly, "Sam Clemens, what are you trying to prove?"

He went to Washington to see the nation's capital, but he didn't find the answer. Winter had frozen the ruts along Pennsylvania Avenue, damp gusts from across the Potomac chilled him to the bone as he toiled up the hill to the Capitol, and the boarding house where he roomed was cramped, cheerless, and drafty. He didn't try to find work, but spent the days in aimless, rather spiritless sight-seeing, blaming his environment for his own inner discontent. Often Henry crept into his thoughts. Those two issues of the *Journal* that Sam had edited while Orion was away had at least tickled Henry. He grinned again at the memory of his younger brother's shrieking glee over "To Miss Katie in H——l."

But then Sam's good humor faded. Henry was just a boy —like himself. Orion was more mature in his judgments and tastes. What they thought was so funny must seem to Orion what doubtless it was—childish lampooning, a sad substitute for the articles by Ralph Waldo Emerson and Oliver Wendell Holmes that he so desperately wanted to publish.

Sam bounced over the rails on his return trip to Philadelphia, feeling the ache of growing pains in his legs and the deeper twinges of growth in his spirit. He knew that he could have his job back on the *Inquirer*, but instead he found new employment on the *Ledger*. One rainy morning he walked along Chestnut Street, thinking about Ma. Did she miss him? Did she realize how alone he could feel, so cut adrift like a rotting barge on the old Mississippi?

"I'm going back to New York," Sam said to the rain beating against his face. He packed that same afternoon and crossed the ferry to Camden, New Jersey, where he caught the night train. Later, he thought what a boyish fool he was to run off on an impulse like this, without going around to say good-by to old Frog and his other friends. And he had upset his landlady by walking out the day after she had put clean sheets on his bed; to her, it was a wicked waste. "She'll turn them, and the next lodger will be no wiser," Sam guessed shrewdly. It was no wonder a yellow-fever epidemic spread quickly.

In New York his spirits picked up. The tigerish little foreman welcomed him back to Gray's, for Sam could now set ten thousand ems a day and that was extremely g-o-o-d. Yet trouble loomed between these two on the day the foreman caught Sam gazing from the window at the ships in the harbor.

"Admiring our beautiful Hudson, Mr. Clemens?" the foreman asked, just a tiny squirt of acid in his voice. Sam shook his head. He had been thinking that fifteen months had passed since his leaving Hannibal. "It is a mighty fine river," the foreman insisted.

Sam's eyes suddenly twinkled. "Fine in its way," he said. "But the Hudson can't hold a candle to the Mississippi!"

"What's that, sir?"

"You take the two," Sam declared, "and the old Mississippi is far and away the b-e-t-t-e-r!"

"Indeed, Mr. Clemens?"

"Why," Sam said, knowing that his valedictory at Gray's should be a good effort, reflecting q-u-a-l-i-t-y in both italics and small caps, "I reckon you could drop the whole Hudson River into the Mississippi, starting maybe at St. Louis, and by the time you reached Memphis not more'n a drop or two would show."

A fringe of color appeared around the edges of the foreman's whiskers, and to spare the explosion, Sam announced quietly that he was leaving.

He was sick of drifting, of living by himself and for himself. He missed Ma. He missed Henry and Orion. He was so rotten homesick that he could walk home, and after sitting up three days and three nights in a smoking car to reach St. Louis, he wished that he had tried it. Then, aboard the *Keokuk Packet*, he slept thirty-six hours without waking and came to in a bubbling mood. What a dazzler of an idea he had for his homecoming!

Ma, Henry, and Orion were eating breakfast when the door of the Keokuk house was flung open. There stood the unexpected Sam—leveling a gun at them. "Ha, Orion!" cried Sam. "You wouldn't let me buy a gun, so I bought one myself, and, heaven bear me witness, you come a step toward me and I'll use it in self-defense!"

Jane Clemens, bursting with laughter, cried joyfully, "You, Sammy! You haven't changed!"

Orion grinned, but had to find a moral. "If it isn't bad enough to exchange your birthright for a mess of pottage, Sam'll do it for a joke!"

Henry leaped from his chair, snatched the gun from Sam and playfully banged its butt against his brother's. "Oh, Sammy, it's so good to have you back. Nothing's the same in this family without you!"

"I guess I'm through wandering," Sam said sheepishly. "And I'm hungry."

16.

Thomas Jefferson Snodgrass

Ma was wrong. Sam had changed. At first, he acted fidgety and went to live with Pamela in St. Louis where he resumed working for the *Evening Post;* then he returned to Keokuk and settled down to helping Orion. Outwardly Sam seemed serene, good-humored, and satisfied with doing the labor of two, yet there were moments, sometimes a day, once even a whole week, when it seemed as though something was boiling up inside that he didn't quite understand himself. One day Ma heard him mutter, "I shouldn't have done it. Frog was an old man, and his legs hurt. I thought it was funny, but it was mean and cruel." Ma asked no questions. Pa had been a great mutterer. She was used to it.

By now Orion had married. True, Orion nearly started on his honeymoon by forgetting to wait for his bride Mollie. "Just like Pa," Sam laughed, remembering the summer when the absent-minded Judge had ridden off to the farm and left Sam in Hannibal. But gradually Orion was learning to pay attention to his plump, aggressive little wife. In a rare stroke of genius, Orion decided to make Sam a partner in the business so that he could share the responsibility for not paying his own wages. Living on the free soil of Iowa was opening up new horizons for Orion, Sam declared.

But no one could have cared less about money than Sam
—after all, he teased Orion, he already had a gun—and he
was happy as long as he could be supplied with enough books
for those periods when a "reading fit" smote him. Sam looked
a ridiculous figure, propped up in bed, a book in his hand,
a Turkish water pipe on the floor, a smoking tube stuck in
his mouth on which he sucked constantly until the pet cat
on his lap smacked at it in the belligerent notion that it
wheezed too much like a mouse. He developed a sly trick
late at night of listening for his younger brother's step on
the stairs and then calling out his name in a wheedling voice.

"Yes, Sam?" Henry asked, popping his head through the
door. "Is something wrong?"

"Light my pipe for me, will you?"

"Why don't you get out of bed and light it yourself?"

"I knew you'd be along, and I thought I'd save myself the
trouble."

"Well, I'll be!" Henry exclaimed, feigning exasperation. He lit the pipe. "What's the book, Sam?"

"Mess of trash that's supposed to be funny. I could write a funnier one."

"Why don't you, Sam?"

"I've been thinking."

Henry sat down on the edge of the bed. "You remember when we were kids, Sam? Remember when we played Catfish that time, and I almost died holding my breath? How did you beat me?"

"I cheated."

"That's what I figured. Were you mixed up in letting those cats loose in the Western Star?"

Sam chuckled. "Greatest trick ever pulled in Hannibal, Henry. Tom Blankenship had the idea—he and Satan were secret partners. Now he's moved to some place in Montana. Guess his Pap heard the likker was free out there."

"You had the real times in Hannibal, Sam." Henry said enviously. "I was always too scared to cut up, but you made the old place hum. I bet sometimes you wish those good times could have lived forever."

Sam sucked vigorously on his pipe, as though seeking to put a screen of smoke between his thoughts and Henry. "Times change, and things are finished," he said, a bit grumpily. "If I'm going to finish this unfunny funny book tonight, I better get at it. Thanks for lighting the pipe, Henry."

" 'Night, Sam."

The ever-deepening affection for Henry was one change in Sam that Ma noticed with real pleasure. She liked, too, the way girls took to him. A streak of the old horseplay remained, but it was tapering off. The music teacher downstairs who complained that Sammy stomped up the steps too noisily had been too sharp-tongued. The next night Sam invited over some cronies, and using some empty wine bottles they found in a trash barrel, they played a game of tenpins with a cannon ball that must have been heard a mile away. The following evening Sam organized a militia company, and they drilled over the teacher's head. By morning the music instructor was waiting for Sam, ready to negotiate a peace treaty. "Mr. Clemens, I don't mind for myself, but the young ladies taking their lessons are greatly disturbed."

Sam prided himself on being a Southern gentleman. "Shucks, Professor, I'm sorry. Apologize for me, will you? Tell them it won't happen again."

"They'll be delighted, Mr. Clemens."

"Shucks, if I had known . . ."

Sam hadn't come by his occasional slyness unnaturally. It was Ma who had told the "Professor" this approach would work. She was learning about her changing Sammy. He was different from anyone she had ever known. He could come into a room full of people, start talking in his lazy drawl, and soon everyone listened raptly.

"Funniest darn thing happened when I was working in the shop last night," Sam began one evening.

Orion looked up from the *Keokuk Post*. "That's strange, Sam. I was there. I didn't notice anything."

"How about those bugs?"

"Yes," Orion admitted soberly, "there were bugs. You get bugs in summer."

"But did you see what those bugs were doing?"

Orion suspected that he was being led into a trap. Pretty Belle Stotts, a youthful cousin of Orion's wife who had a crush on Sam, asked eagerly, "What? Tell us!"

"You all really want to know?" teased Sam, looking straight at prettier Annie Taylor, on whom he had a crush.

Ma laughed. "Bugs are bugs."

"Well, maybe," Sam drawled, "but last night I stood at

the little press until nearly two o'clock, and the flaring gas-light over my head attracted all the varieties of bugs found in natural history, and all with the same praiseworthy reck-lessness about flying into the fire. At first they came in little sociable crowds of a dozen or so, but soon increased in numbers, until a religious meeting of several millions assem-bled on the board before me, presided over by a venerable beetle who occupied the most prominent lock of my hair as his chair of state. Innumerable lesser dignitaries of the same tribe clustered around him, keeping order, and at the same time endeavoring to attract the attention of the vast assemblage to their own importance by grating their teeth.

"It must have been an interesting occasion—perhaps a great bug jubilee commemorating the triumph of the locusts over Pharaoh's crops in Egypt many centuries ago. At least good seats, commanding an unobstructed view, were in great demand, and small fortunes were made by certain delegates from Yankeeland by disposing of comfortable places on my shoulders at round premiums. In fact, the advantages which my altitude afforded were so well appreciated I began to look like one of those big cards in the museum with bugs impaled on pins."

Sam paused, and Henry tiptoed over with the Turkish water pipe and thrust the tube into Sam's mouth so that he looked like an Oriental potentate.

"What happened then, Sam?" Belle Stotts pleaded.

"Well," Sam said, nodding to Henry to watch the pipe and see that it stayed lighted, "the big 'president' beetle rose and ducked his head and, crossing his arms over his shoulders, stroked them down the tip of his nose several times, and after thus disposing of the perspiration, stuck his hands under his wings, propped his back against a lock of hair, and bob-bing his head at the congregation, remarked, 'B-u-z-z!' To which the congregation devoutly responded, 'B-u-z-z!'

"Satisfied with this promptness on the part of his flock, he took a more perpendicular pose against another lock of my hair and, lifting his hands to command silence, gave another melodious 'b-u-z-z!' on a louder key (which I suppose to have been the keynote) and after a moment's silence the whole congregation burst into a grand anthem. Three dignified daddy-longlegs, perched near the gas burner, beat quadruple time during the performance.

"Soon two parts of the great chorus maintained silence, while a treble and alto duet, sung by forty-seven thousand mosquitoes and twenty-three thousand houseflies, came in; and then, after another chorus, a tenor and bass duet by thirty-two thousand locusts and ninety-seven thousand pinch bugs was sung; then another grand chorus, 'Let Every Bug Rejoice and Sing' (we sing 'heart' instead of 'bug') terminated the performance, during which eleven treble singers split their throats from heads to heels, and the patriotic 'daddies' who beat time hadn't a stump of a leg left."

Eyes twinkling, Sam sucked placidly on the water pipe, and Ma understood a bit more about how he was different. Bugs were bugs to her and Orion and Henry, but they only saw as far as the end of their noses. Months before it happened, Ma realized that Sam's itch to wander would return. She was quite prepared when, about two years after he had come to Keokuk, he approached her with a new idea.

"Ma, you read about how they've been exploring the Amazon?"

"My eyes are getting weak, Sammy. I don't read as much as I ought."

"There're fortunes to be made in cocoa plantations, Ma."

Jane Clemens sighed. The Tennessee land or the Amazon —what did it matter that a few thousand miles separated them? "When are you leaving, Sam?"

"I'll have to think on that a bit. Worst thing that bothers me is how to break the news to Orion."

"Shouldn't think that would be so hard, Sammy. If you could tell me you were going to St. Louis when you intended to go to New York, I don't see why you can't tell Orion you're going to New York and keep on going till you reach the Amazon."

" 'Tis kind of simple."

Jane Clemens smiled. "Well, you're not, Sammy. You're as complicated as a fine watch. That's why, I guess, I know you have to keep running."

"I reckon I'll straighten out after a time and see whatever it is that I'm supposed to."

"Maybe the bugs will tell you, Sam—likely they've got smarter bugs on the Amazon. What I'd like to know is where you'll find the money to go."

"That's something I've still got to talk over with the Lord," Sam said with a grin. But he had ideas. One of them carried him to the desk of the managing editor of the *Keokuk Post*, a kindly gentleman whose eyes seemed even softer under the green eyeshade he wore.

"You're Orion's brother, aren't you? You're Sam Clemens."

"Well, yes, and no," Sam said.

"What's yes about it?"

"I am Sam Clemens, and I am Orion's brother."

"And what's the no?"

"As far as you're concerned, I'd like to be somebody else."

The editor nodded. "That figures. Whole town of Keokuk's crazy. You'll make a fine mayor some day, Clemens. What will *I* call you?"

"If you don't mind, since I took a hankering to the jingle in it, I'd like you to know me as Thomas Jefferson Snodgrass."

"Jehoshaphat!"

Sam drawled that maybe he'd better explain. He was going on a trip, perhaps as far as the Amazon. He wanted to send back letters that the *Keokuk Post* might publish.

"But why sign them Thomas Jefferson Snodgrass?" the editor persisted. "Why not just plain Sam Clemens?"

"Well," Sam said guilelessly, "Orion might not like it. You see, these are going to be funny letters."

"Funny to whom?"

"To me—or I won't send them."

"What do you figure I ought to pay for them?"

"Nothing, I suppose."

"Well, that's dirt cheap, I must say. Is this Clemens or Snodgrass talking?"

"Clemens. Snodgrass wants five dollars a piece."

"If I use 'em."

Sam nodded. He was almost out the door when the editor shouted, "Say, Clemens, tell Snodgrass not to make those letters too long. Stupid people in Keokuk only have two eyes in their heads."

"I'll tell him," Sam promised and went happily into the sunlight. Later, walking along Main Street, he saw a sheet of paper fluttering in the breeze, as once he had seen the drifting leaf from the book about Joan of Arc. Sam looked at it, gulped, plunged it into his pocket and raced home.

"A fifty-dollar bank note!" Jane Clemens exclaimed. "Well, I never!"

"Me, neither!"

"Sammy, I'd like to think that the Lord woke up this morning and said, 'That Sam Clemens's been good enough to be surprised with a miracle,' but I doubt it. More likely it was on a counting-table in some bank or business office, and the wind swept it out the window."

"You think I'll have to advertise to find the owner?"

"I'm afraid so, Sammy."

In later years Sam, who never hesitated to twist facts if it made a better story, declared, "I advertised the find and left for the Amazon the same day."

As Sam traveled to Chicago, Indianapolis, and Cincinnati, where he had a choice of connections to New York or New Orleans, it was difficult to tell who was using the passage ticket—Sam Clemens or Thomas Jefferson Snodgrass. Sam remembered the futile evenings in Philadelphia when his writing could claim no spark of life, because he was trying to please everyone but himself. This time he would put on paper people as he saw them and heard them and believed them to be. Long before he reached Cincinnati he and Snodgrass had agreed on an appropriate opening:

> You know arter going down there to St. Louis, and seein' so many wonderful things, I wanted to see more—so I took a notion to go a travelin', so as to see the world, and then write a book about it—a kind o' daily journal like—and have all in gold on the back of it, "Snodgrass' Dierrea," or somethin' of that kind, like other authors that visits forren parts.

Sam grinned. Would Henry remember? He had said that maybe one of these days Sam would write a funny book. In a way, Thomas Jefferson Snodgrass was W. Epaminondas Adrastus Blab come back to life—a distant cousin no doubt, who had seen more of America than poor old Blab, who never had gone farther from Hannibal than a hop and a skip in a skiff to Glasscock's Island. Sam stood beside Thomas Jefferson Snodgrass in the Chicago depot and chronicled that hero's struggle over ticket and luggage.

> . . . bimeby my vallis made its appearance, with shirts and cravats hangin out one end, and socks and collars at t'other lookin considerable like an Irishman that's jest got out of a

New Orleans 'lection riot—and dern my cats if I'd a knowed it was my vallis at all!

Sam and Snodgrass accepted the hazards of the subsequent journey in high spirits.

I went down one night to the railroad office there, purty close onto the Laclede House, and bought about a quire o' yaller paper, cut up into tickets—one for each railroad in the United States, I thought, but I found out afterwards that the Alexandria and Boston Air-Line was left out—and then got a baggage feller to take my trunk down to the boat where he spilled it out on the levee, bustin' it open and shakin' out the contents, consisting of "guides" to Chicago, and "guides" to Cincinnati, and travelers' guides, and all kinds of sich books, not excepting a "guide to heaven," which last aint much use to a feller in Chicago, I kin tell you. Finally, the fast packet quit ringing her bell, and started down the river—but she hadn't gone mor'n a mile, till she ran clean up on top of a sand-bar, whar she stuck till plum one o'clock, spite of the Captain's swearin'—and they had to set the whole crew to cussin' at last afore they got her off.

Sam disembarked at Cincinnati and, needing to bolster his resources for the journey to the Amazon, found employment almost at once in the printing office of Wrightson & Company. Next, he secured lodging in a boarding house that claimed the one virtue he insisted upon; it was cheap. "If I find anyone in this place to talk with, the Lord will have to work another miracle," Sam mumbled, already feeling the loneliness of the impending long winter evenings. Perhaps he was heard in heaven.

Cincinnati would never know a more diverse pair of friends than Sam and the mysterious Scotsman Macfarlane, who left the boarding house promptly at six each morning and returned as promptly at six each evening. Sam was frank,

disarming, boyishly eager; Macfarlane was secretive, crotch-
ety, and overflowing with middle-aged cynicism. Though
his hands were hardened and soiled from mechanical labor,
he offered no clue to his occupation. Grilling a herring for
the two of them to eat, Macfarlane merely waved a hand
at the books on history, philosophy, science, and religion
that cluttered his room. He wanted Sam to know him only
as a self-made scholar and philosopher—a dour Scotch one
at that. Evening after evening their debates were brisk, sharp,
and scarcely the type of discussion heard in the parlors of
Hannibal and Keokuk.

"Life!" sniffed Macfarlane, disgusted with the subject before he started. "What is it?"

"Thomas Jefferson Snodgrass would say that, at best, life's
'discouragin',"' Sam said.

"Who in tarnation is Snodgrass?"

"Friend of mine," Sam answered vaguely, filled with serious doubts as to whether Snodgrass was ready to enter a
world that also contained Macfarlane.

"You tell your friend for me," the Scotsman said, jabbing
angrily with his fork at the herring, "that he probably doesn't
know anything about life at all."

"I'm afraid you're right."

"Of course, I'm right! Life developed over the ages from
a microscopic seed germ—one, if you like, that the Creator
planted in the dawn of time—and from that seed man developed."

In England a chap named Charles Darwin would have
understood what Macfarlane meant, and doubtless would
have been a mite upset, since Darwin had yet to become
famous by publishing his theory of evolution.

"At least man got here after a time," Sam said, taking the
cheerful view.

"More's the pity," Macfarlane snapped. "Bad blunder man

was, all the way through. Got the only bad heart in the animal kingdom."

"You make it sound terrible."

"Not horrible enough. What other animal is so capable of malice as man? So vindictive? So likely to get drunk—mean, nasty drunk? Show me any other animal that can stand being as unclean as a man!"

"Man thinks he belongs at the top of the heap among animals."

The Scotsman's eyes glittered. He rubbed his hardened hands excitedly.

"Man's at the bottom of the animal kingdom," Macfarlane cried. "Part of the mud and the slime. He's depraved, not only enslaving other animals but also members of his own race!"

Night after night, all through the winter, the discussions continued. Macfarlane read from his books, then flung them at Sam to read for himself. Even though the *Keokuk Post* had published two letters, Sam decided to bury Thomas Jefferson Snodgrass quietly. What immature, senseless, little-boy blatherings he had concocted! He hid the copies of the paper in which Snodgrass had enjoyed his brief fling, so that Macfarlane might not read them and guess the identity of the ass who had written such drivel. A twinge of his earlier affection for Snodgrass stabbed at his heart, but the cynicism the Scotsman was teaching him made him look at himself with contempt. Unhappily, he also was a member of the family of man.

Spring rushed upon Cincinnati. By late March, the grass was green, leaves unfurled on the trees, flowers burst into bloom. Macfarlane hated to leave his books and evening herring, but one night Sam wheedled him into a stroll along the Ohio River, a link to his beloved Mississippi. The Scotsman listened to Sam's prattle about the glory of the river and her tributaries until his dour scowl dipped toward his shoetops. "Enough about your blasted ditch! Tell me no more! The Ohio's a sewer. The Mississippi's the same. That's all they are, a great sewer!"

Sam laughed. "You may know more about life than I do, but I know more about the river."

"Only human scum travels the steamers!"

"I didn't think there was anything else."

Macfarlane snorted. "You say that to a Scotsman, who grew up among the English, Welsh, and Irish! Great Godfrey, Clemens—use some discretion!"

"You're all part of one empire."

Macfarlane seemed on the verge of losing his sanity. "Everything a Scotsman does is voluntary—remember that! We live under English laws, but only because we approve of them. We fight in England's wars, but if we had a mind to, we'd negotiate a separate treaty with the enemy."

Sam wondered if, like Macfarlane, all Scotsmen got their opinions directly from God.

"How I pity you, Sam—what you're just beginning to go through. You think you've got much to learn, but you've got more to unlearn. You've been brought up to think man uses words as a poet, but they forget to tell you he uses the same words to cheat, to betray, to plot evil. They teach you that man is a marvel who invents tools to build houses and cities, but the same man fashions weapons of war to knock down other houses and wipe out other cities." Macfarlane practically wept. "The great unlearning is ahead for you, laddie, and a miserable period it is!"

All the way back to the boarding house Macfarlane bemoaned man's duplicity, but Sam only smelled the flowers, recalling the wonderful fragrance of the locust trees in Hannibal when spring stole up the old river.

In April of 1857, he bade a reluctant farewell to Macfarlane and went on his way, knowing at last why he wandered—not to learn, but to unlearn.

In New Orleans some of the fastest unlearning of his lifetime awaited him. Nobody could say that a ship ever had, would, or should leave New Orleans for the Amazon! Dismayed, Sam roamed aimlessly through the city, until he stumbled upon a graveyard in the heart of town.

He was particularly drawn to the tomb of a seventeen-year-old girl. "They say that the flowers upon many of these tombs are replaced by fresh ones every day," he wrote Ma. "These were fresh and the poor girl had been dead *five years*. There's depth of affection! On another was the inscription, 'To My Dear Mother,' with fresh flowers. The lady was 62 years old when she died, and she had been dead *seven years!*"

If Macfarlane could have read over Sam's shoulder, he would have turned away with disgust. Sam was a total loss —sentimental, tenderhearted, in love with life!

17.
Bixby's Cub

Even the cemeteries in New Orleans added to the charm and mystery of the city. Sam marveled how the graveyard was laid out in straight little streets. White shells glistened in the paths, and the sun sparkled brightly on the marble of the imposing tombs. In Hannibal or Keokuk people were buried under the ground and soon forgotten. Here, their remains rested in tombs above the ground and were honored with vases of fresh flowers and statuettes; one tomb had even a lace curtain in front. Many of the inscriptions were in French, and trying to decipher them, Sam shook his head. They seemed as strange to him as the orange and magnolia trees he passed.

He came out into the narrow, crisscrossed passages of the French Quarter and wandered down into its great market. He saw two girls sipping coffee with their beaus in one of the outdoor stalls, and thought that it would do his very boots good to meet Belle Stotts or Annie Taylor or a dozen other Keokuk girls whose faces flashed across his memory.

Sam sauntered through the French Market, struck by its cleanliness and neatness. Pyramids of fruit—oranges, lemons, pineapples, bananas, figs, plantains, watermelons, blackberries, raspberries, plums—tempted him to part with some of his slim resources. Next to them were piles of radishes, onions, squashes, peas, beans, sweet potatoes; then stalls filled with lobsters, oysters, and clams. Vendors hawked milk, cheese, cakes, coffee, tea, nuts, apples, hot rolls, butter, meats, and poultry.

Men, women, and children jammed the market, and Sam wrote Ma, "Out on the pavement were groups of Italians, French, Dutch, Irish, Spaniards, Indians, Chinese, Americans, English, and the Lord knows how many different kinds of people, selling all kinds of articles—even clothing of every description, from a handkerchief down to a pair of boots, umbrellas, pins, combs, matches—in fact, anything you could possibly want—and keeping up a terrible din with their various cries."

In the midst of this bedlam, Sam wrangled with his problem. Since he had earned his keep as a typesetter in New York and Philadelphia, St. Louis and Cincinnati, there was no reason why he couldn't make out as well in New Orleans. But going back to another printing office seemed to him a dead end—almost a tomb above the ground. That prospect certainly did not satisfy the old something inside him that now, stronger than ever, boiled and heaved.

He could forget the Amazon with a snap of his fingers, but not the fortune he had expected to make from his cocoa plantation. Why did he want the money? For himself? Truthfully, he could shake his head. No, he wanted the money for Ma and Orion and Henry. Look how he had sweated for Orion in Hannibal and Keokuk, not caring where day ended and night began, caring less if he never received his wages. Why? Because Orion needed capital, a chance just once to do something more than grub along, defeated before his life started.

Thinking of Orion, of those first early struggles with the *Journal* in Hannibal, Sam's memory suddenly exploded.

Vividly, he was once again back in that dear old, rowdy
hog-drovers' paradise—with Tom and Bence and Will and
Pet and Wales—and with old John Hannicks, glimpsing that
first smudge of smoke around the point and letting out a
whoop: "Steeammm-*boat* a-comin'!" The old river! That
was it! Deep in his heart, the will, the drive, the insight, the
ideal had been locked away, waiting to be found. He would
be a Mississippi River pilot—a king on the old river!

With Sam, wishes still became necessities. He was off in
a dash for the levee. The instant he saw the paddle-wheeler
Paul Jones cruising in the river, an inner voice whispered,
"Sam Clemens, there's your boat!" He found his way aboard,
ignored the suspicious scrutiny of the mate, and entered the
wheelhouse. "Good mornin'," he said pleasantly to the man
at the wheel.

Horace Bixby looked sharply over the bow at the head
of Island No. 35. "Good morning, sir," he answered, brisk
in his courtesy. He didn't bother to turn around.

Sam drew a deep breath. "How would you like a young
man to learn the river?"

"I wouldn't like it."

"Why not?"

"Cub pilots are more trouble than they're worth."

"Can you have pilots without having cubs first?"

"I can." But Bixby turned, and looked at the slender,
loose-limbed young fellow whose bush of hair had turned
auburn. Now that he was entering his twenties, Sam's fair
complexion gave him an almost girlish appearance. The pilot
humphed to himself. Angels on the outside were usually
the biggest devils underneath.

"I'm a printer by trade," Sam said. "I thought I'd go to
South America. But I'd like piloting better."

Bixby's glance returned to the head of Island No. 35.
"Where'd you get that lazy drawl?"

"From my Ma."

"Where'd you grow up?"

"Hannibal."

"Know the Bowen boys there?"

"I sure did—young Will was almost my best friend."

"Older brother Bart's a fine pilot. What's your name?"

"Clemens. Pump handle's Sam."

Bixby stared unwaveringly at the river. "You drink?"

"No."

"Gamble?"

"No."

"Swear?"

"Not for amusement."

Sam couldn't see Bixby's grin. "You chew?"

"No—but I smoke. Bad as though I had a boiler in me."

"Ever do any steering?"

"I've steered just about every kind of boat there is on this river—except a steamboat."

Bixby turned round again. He had a sore foot and he wanted more than anything to sit on the bench and rest. "Here," he said, "take the wheel, and we'll see what you can do with a steamboat."

"You mean—now?"

"Don't expect to be here next week. Keep her as she is— aiming toward that lower cottonwood snag."

Sam took the wheel, his heart in his throat. The paddles of the *Paul Jones* churned, her boilers sizzled, her engines throbbed. He could feel Bixby's eyes on him and the river, watching both carefully. Yet he must be doing all right for in an easy voice the pilot explained that he wouldn't take on a cub unless he was paid for training him. He'd want five hundred dollars and no responsibility for the cub's expenses off duty.

"I could pay you in land in Tennessee," Sam said. "Maybe

give you two thousand acres out of my share of what Pa left."

"No, thank you. I've got too much unimproved real estate already."

Sam thought of Pamela and her husband. They could lend him something when he reached St. Louis. "Suppose I gave you a hundred dollars cash and the rest when I earn it?"

"All right. Get your duds on board as soon as you can. And give me back the wheel." Bixby saw the bright, shining eagerness in Sam's face and wondered if he'd last a week.

"Thank you, sir," Sam exclaimed.

Bixby harumphed to himself, then answered, "Thank your Ma for giving you that pleasant drawl. That's what decided me!"

To Bixby's surprise and Sam's own amazement the cub lasted the first week and was still lasting when the *Paul Jones* had steamed eight hundred miles up the river from New Orleans. What he had learned during this time was that bearded, goggle-eyed, tough-minded Horace Bixby was essentially a kind man for all his occasional flashes of short temper and irascibility, and that he, Sam Clemens, was about as bright as an empty whisky cask drifting on the river. "Sam," barked Bixby, now that they were inside the old sycamore snag and safe for a time, "tell me the shape of Walnut Bend."

"Why not ask me the condition of my grandmother's left hip after the train hit her?" Sam moaned.

"We passed it this morning."

"Did we?"

"Remember I pointed out the China trees to you?"

Sam nodded vaguely.

Bixby clamped both hands tight on the wheel. His sore foot still ached, but not so badly as his patience. "I've told you, Sam. You've got to get fixed in your mind the whole

shape of this river. Every bend. Where every sand bar is.
Every tree snag. And when they change, and where, and
why."

"I'm tryin'."

"You've got to get *two* pictures of this river fixed in your
mind. The river looks one way by day and another at night."

"Catfish and kittens!" Sam exploded.

"Save your energy for learning," Bixby advised wryly.
"Let me see what you wrote in your notebook this morning."

Sam handed him the soiled, crumpled document. The pilot
went through the dozens of cramped, penciled notations,
bobbing his head in approval and muttering, "You've got
that right . . . by great Caesar's ghost, don't you ever forget
the slack water off those cottonwoods . . ." Then he stopped
with a snort as he read the entry.

MERIWEATHER'S BEND

¼ less 3—run shape of upper bar and go into the low place
in the willows about 100 feet lower down than last year.

For the next minute Bixby turned the air in the wheelhouse blue. "The one quarter less three fathoms is right, but
I told you, I told you, I told you '*two* hundred lower down
than last year.' Do you hear me, Sam? Say something!"

"I wish I were dead," Sam said.

"You may be, if you turn there. Here, correct it! And
study it all when you're off watch." Bixby flung the book
across the wheelhouse.

Four hours on, four hours off—so Sam learned to live
around the clock. Now, finishing the watch with Bixby, he
sat by the rail, notebook in hand, trying to cram its contents
into his brain. There were four-hour gaps in the images of
the river as he had seen it from the wheelhouse, since his

notes only covered his time on watch with the pilot. Next trip, when his watch changed, he'd have to fill them in. "And learn it all over," he groaned, "or forget it all over!" He squinted in the sun. How could he ever master it? It would be easier to learn the New Testament, even if he set out to recite it backward.

Beyond him, the leadsman was croaking out the sounding. "Half twain! half twain! half twain! half twain! half twain!" He was like the old clock that stood in the family room at the Quarles farm, the most infernal tick-tocker ever, if you were trying to concentrate. But the good smell of the river rose into the cub's nostrils, and Sam thought a little hopefully, Some of it'll stick. There must be some glue with the sawdust in my cranium.

Yet, at one phase of life on the Mississippi the cub excelled at once. The crew thought it had already crowned its champion liars, but Sam refused to back down to anybody.

Off duty with Sam were two deck hands and a mate, full of lip, and the mate hold how back home he'd been the fire chief and had saved more people than lived in Missouri, Arkansas, and three quarters of Texas. His stories grew pretty reckless in their claims, so Sam put down his notebook, and waited till the mate sucked in his breath like an old fire pumper.

"Boys, I had great presence of mind once," he said, with a dead pan. "It was at a fire. An old man was leaning out of a four-story building, calling for help. Everybody in the crowd below looked up, but nobody did anything, because the ladders weren't long enough. Nobody had any presence of mind—nobody but me. I came to the rescue. I yelled for a rope. When it came I threw the end of it to the old man. He caught it, and I told him to tie it around his waist. He did so, and I pulled him down."

The deck hands roared, and the mate stomped off. Sam, undisturbed, returned to his study.

Sometimes Sam stood watch with George Ealer, who was Bixby's "partner," as rivermen insisted on calling the "other pilot" on a boat. Sam never loved a man more. Ealer was gentle, minimized all mistakes, and declared that Sam was coming along twice as fast as he really was. "You're a liar," Sam said. He could talk that way to Ealer.

"I'm not saying being a pilot isn't tough," Ealer admitted. "A Mississippi River pilot can get paid as much as the Vice-President of the United States—a pilot with an A-1 rating, that is. I guess maybe he should sweat a little."

For all his mildness, Ealer could set a hard task. He would often turn the wheel over to Sam when they approached a levee where several other boats were tied up.

"How close shall I come to them, sir?"

"About as close as you'd peel an apple."

"Go on!"

"I mean it. You've not got the water otherwise."

"What if I hit?"

"You can't ram!"

"Just tell me why?"

"Because, Sam, without courage and quick, sound judgment you can't be a pilot!" So Sam peeled the other boats and nudged in against the levee, and Ealer said, "See—you made it!"

"I guess so," Sam replied. "I haven't opened my eyes yet."

At night, tossing in his bunk when he should have been sleeping between watches, Sam called himself ten thousand fools for trying to chew a whole hog instead of a strip of bacon. Not if he lived to be as old as Aunt Nell said she was would he make a pilot! He listened to the gay, unsuspecting chatter of the passengers and hoped they could swim. They'd need to when Bixby made him steer that night, and he split the *Paul Jones* in two on a cottonwood snag. Or he thought of the valuable cargo and wondered if the insurance agents threw a cub pilot in jail after he sank an entire load in six feet of Mississippi mud.

Yet, he did learn. In all Sam's life no achievement ever gave him so much satisfaction. He described the real nature of that accomplishment in one of his books.

It is a tremendous thing to know every trivial detail of twelve hundred miles of river and know it with absolute exactness. If you will take the longest street in New York, and travel up and down it, conning its features patiently until you know every house and window and lamppost and big and little sign by heart, and know them so accurately that you can instantly name the one you are abreast of when you are set down at random in that street in the middle of an inky black night, you will then have a tolerable notion of the amount and the exactness of a pilot's knowledge who carries the Mississippi River in his head. And then, if you will go on until you know every street-crossing, the character, size, and position of the crossing-stones, and the varying depth of the mud in each of these numberless places, you will have some idea of what the pilot must know in order to keep a Mississippi steamer out of trouble. Next, if you will take half of the signs in that long street, and *change their places* once a month, and still manage to know their new positions accurately on dark nights, and keep up with these repeated changes without making any mistakes, you will understand what is required of a pilot's peerless memory by the fickle Mississippi.

Still, Sam was no shameless braggart. In the end his triumph was won rather easily, and he explained why.

How comfortably the pilot's memory does its work; how placidly effortless is its way; how *unconsciously* it lays up its vast stores, hour by hour, day by day, and never loses or mislays a single valuable package of them all! Take an instance. Let a leadsman cry, "Half twain! half twain! half twain! half twain! half twain!" until it becomes as monotonous as the ticking of a clock; let conversation be going on all the time, and the pilot be doing his share of the talking, and no longer consciously listening to the leadsman; and in the midst of this endless string of half twains let a single "quarter twain!" be interjected, without emphasis, and then the half-twain cry go on again, just as before; two or three weeks later that pilot can describe with precision the boat's position in the river when that quarter twain was uttered, and give you such a lot of head-marks, stern-marks, and side-marks to guide you, that you ought to be able to take the boat there and put her in that same spot again yourself! The cry of "quarter twain" did not really take his mind from his talk, but his trained faculties instantly photographed the bearings, noted the change of depth, and laid up the important details for further reference without requiring any assistance from *him* in the matter. If you were walking and talking with a friend, and another friend at your side kept up a monotonous repetition of the vowel sound A, for a couple of blocks, and then in the midst interjected an R, thus, A, A, A, A, A, R, A, A, A, etc., and gave the R no emphasis, you would not be able to state, two or three weeks afterward, that the R had been put in, nor be able to tell what objects you were passing at the moment it was done. But you could, if your memory had been patiently and laboriously trained to do that sort of thing mechanically.

On the other hand, for Sam to ask Bixby at eight what he had eaten for breakfast at seven-thirty was a waste of time. The pilot never remembered.

The high wages paid on the Missouri River runs began to make Bixby's palms itch, and one day he told Sam that he was going to quit the Mississippi for a time.

"What happens to me, sir?" Sam asked, for river custom gave Bixby the right to assign him to another pilot during his absence.

"Beck Jolly's taking you. On the *John J. Roe*."

"That old trading scow! You want me to learn how to fall asleep while steering?"

Bixby chuckled. "Beck does all the sleeping. I guess you'll keep awake."

Reluctantly, Sam transferred to his new berth, beginning with a scowl the happiest river days he would ever know. The *Roe* was a freight boat exclusively, owned by farmers who kept it for their own use. River gossip that she was "as slow as an island and as comfortable as a farm" described her perfectly.

"Slow she is," Beck Jolly declared, laughing harder than anyone. "Put her downstream and she can't quite overtake the current." Years later, when the *Roe* sank off New Madrid, Sam joked that the owners had grown so accustomed to her tardiness that they waited five years before they inquired into what had happened to her.

But for fun, for hospitality, for life on the old Mississippi at its leisurely best, the *Roe* was a floating paradise. Passengers she did not carry; "family guests" she did, a dozen or so every trip. Her boiler deck was fine for dancing in the moonlight, and there was a piano in her cabin. The work was easy, but the frolicking left even a young fellow tuckered out in the morning. Soon Sam found himself hoping that Bixby would never lose interest in the big money on the Missouri.

Among Sam's other duties under Beck was learning a song about a horse named Methusalem that jingled along:

> Took him down and sold him in Jerusalem,
> A long time ago.

It took forty-eight stanzas to chronicle Methusalem's epic. When it was finished, Sam, rolling over on his back in the moonlight, swore that if somebody didn't pour sweet cider down his throat, he was going to die.

"Can't let that happen, Sammy," Beck Jolly said, obliging his cub. "Got a sweet young girl up yonder hankering to dance with you."

"Beck," Sam sighed, "you reckon there's another boat on the Mississippi as lovely as this?"

"There ain't never been, an' there won't be ag'in."

"I hope Bixby stays contented up there on the Missouri."

"Not forever. Bix's greedy, but that Missouri run's dull. He'll get his craw full of it sooner or later."

"Death and desolation!"

"Mebbe it would be a good thing if he got fed up quick," Beck said seriously. "Kind of things you need to know 'bout the river for your pilot's license you ain't learning here."

Sam didn't argue the point. Instead, he set off across the boiler deck, looking for that "sweet young girl up yonder hankering to dance."

Not more than a week later Sam was steering in the wheel-house when Beck Jolly roused himself from his noonday nap on the bench. "Sam, I hear Bix's coming back."

"How soon?"

"He should be in St. Louis by the time we crawl up there."

Sam stared down at the shimmering water and fought off a wave of sadness. "Beck," he said feelingly, "I won't ever forget you."

There was no answer, and Sam turned. Beck was napping again. Still, Beck smiled gently—rivermen usually heard what they thought they should. Sam grinned. "Looks like slack water ahead," he said suddenly.

Beck jumped up as though shot from a cannon. "Where, Sam? Shouldn't be any slack water on this reach of the river!"

"There isn't," Sam confessed. "I just wanted to see if you're worth your pay."

Beck Jolly settled back on the bench. "Glad Bix's coming back," he growled. "That's the nearest I ever come to heart failure!"

Horace Bixby lasted two trips on the Mississippi before the itch for Missouri money tickled his palm again. "You hear about that new steamer *Pennsylvania*, Sam?" he asked.

"She's supposed to be the queen of the river."

"And she is. Fellow name of Brown pilots her. I'm putting you on her as steersman. Considering that you haven't been on the river a year, I'd say you were coming along at a bound."

Sam nodded, pleased. So within two months he made his second transfer, at St. Louis. The spic-and-span *Pennsylvania*, with her bright trim and eight boilers, looked to be everything rivermen claimed. Sam, his heart pounding, climbed up to the wheelhouse. "I'm Clemens," he said, introducing himself to Brown.

The man turned, exuding arrogance. His big underlip curled, and his little eyes narrowed. "So," he said in a contemptuous voice, "you're Horace *Bigs*by's cub." Almost everyone along the river pronounced Bixby's name as though it were spelled Bigsby, but Brown alone gave his voice a slurring undertone that suggested something unsavory in Bixby's past.

Sam knew then that as long as he lived he was going to hate this man.

18.

River Feud

"WHERE were you born, Clemens?"

"Florida, Missouri."

"You should have stayed there," Brown growled and, turning back to the wheel, spat out the window.

Joy to you, Mr. Brown, Sam thought. May your tribe perish.

After a week on the *Pennsylvania*, Sam decided that everything Macfarlane had ever said about man's low place in the animal kingdom applied to Brown. Just imagine, Sam wrote Henry, "a middle-aged, long, slim, bony, smooth-shaven, horse-faced, ignorant, mote-magnifying tyrant," and that's Brown.

Perhaps Bixby, Ealer, and Beck Jolly were as much to blame as anyone for Sam's bitter comedown. They had spoiled Sam by treating him as a human being, which in Brown's estimation was a frightful mistake to make with any cub. His method was to pick—day, night, every watch —considering wasted any thrust that didn't draw blood. Nor would he give a wound a chance to heal. Once each watch he flung the same complaint at Sam. "I train you, and *Bigs*by gets the money."

"All I know about the river," Sam answered stiffly, "I learned from Bixby, Ealer, and Beck Jolly."

"Jolly? That slob of a cuttlefish—what does he know?"

"How to be a gentleman, sir. Even in the wheelhouse."

Sam, taking the measure of the pilot, found only one attribute to respect in him. Like all pilots, Brown possessed a sharp eye for detail on the river; but his eye was equally proficient in spotting a mean detail in a person. He couldn't describe anyone as tall or short, fair or dark, pleasant or unpleasant, without adding that he had warty hands, squint eyes, a gimpy leg, bad tonsils, false teeth, or a nagging wife.

Each day brought out a new facet of Brown's disagreeable personality. If he sent Sam on an errand, he always greeted the cub's return with the same snarl: "What kept you, Clemens? Did you catch a snooze on the way back? Don't give me another of your wild excuses. I know—I won't forget!" If Sam took the wheel, Brown cursed him and shoved him aside, roaring, "Get away from here! If you handle the *Pennsylvania* round this bend, we'll all go to the bottom!" But if Sam came into the wheelhouse and hesitated, awaiting orders, Brown's tirade was no less blistering. "Fool! Numbskull! Take the wheel! Orders you want? Bah! Why did *Bigs*by ever think he could make a pilot out of you? The money, that's it! *Bigs*by's always got his claw out for a dollar!" When Sam tended the fire in the wheelhouse stove, Brown swung on him, thundering savagely, "Put down that shovel! Can't you see I'm roasting now?" The pilot's words came out in a frosty stream of breath. He couldn't even lie reasonably.

Ealer served as the other pilot on the *Pennsylvania*. By glance and smile he sympathized with Sam, but the code of the river stopped him from interfering in a fellow pilot's treatment of a cub, or from expressing adverse criticism. Ealer's own cub was an easygoing, red-haired, observant

Irish lad named George Ritchie, who had not yet been trained to such fine points in containing his incensed feelings.

"Sam," Ritchie muttered, "I wouldn't blame you if you pitched into Brown. You could whip him. With all that big mouth, he's probably yellow underneath."

"You know how long I'd last afterward? Strike a pilot in the wheelhouse, and you're through."

"But why does he do it?"

"Look at him," Sam said bitterly. "Everybody's afraid of his tongue—you, me, Ealer, the crew. Captain Klinefelter could curb him, but he stays in his cabin during the periods Brown's on duty, avoiding an ugly scene. So Brown's really the master of the finest boat afloat on the Mississippi, the all-powerful despot over all he surveys, and he loves it!"

Ritchie scowled. "I don't know how you take it, Sam."

"I'll tell you how. By staying awake at night, trying to decide which way to kill Brown. I've got seventeen good ways so far, each different. That's how I take it, Ritchie, and by Godfrey if Brown doesn't watch out, maybe I will kill him!"

Or quit the river, Sam had been thinking at other times. Yet in another six months he should be able to qualify for his pilot's license. A dozen tyrants weren't going to keep him from that! "If it takes ten years, I'll get it in spite of him," Sam, more tough-fibered than Brown thought, growled to himself.

The poles of Sam's world now became New Orleans and St. Louis, where, for a few hours each trip, he could escape from thirty-five consecutive days of Brown's invective and abuse. He enjoyed most his time with Pamela and her husband, who understood what he was going through and tried to make each visit in St. Louis a gay respite. On his second trip from New Orleans under Brown, an unexpected pleas-

ure awaited him at Pamela's. Henry had come down from
Keokuk.

The brothers planned a day roaming through the city—
laughing at fellow passengers on the horsecars, taking the
measure of the girls they saw and arguing over which was
prettiest, wandering along the levee where the steamers were
thicker than flies on a watermelon rind. Sam took Henry to
lunch in a place off the levee which was frequented by rivermen. Under Bixby, Ealer, and Beck Jolly, Sam had always
felt decently treated here—for a cub. He had been ribbed,
but the rivermen knew that Bixby, Ealer, or Jolly would
settle the account if the horsing went too far. Brown offered
a cub no such protection.

The comments of the more inebriated off-duty rivermen
became more and more nasty. They laughed unpleasantly at
Henry's girlish fairness, and swore that Sam should stand
them to a round at the bar. "An' none o' your lip, Clemens,"
a burly-built fellow, a mate on the *Amulet*, growled as he
leaned over Sam's table. "Brown's told me what a broken-
down keelboatman's mistake you are! If ever the likes o'
you gets to be a pilot, I'll quit the river."

Sam hesitated. He wasn't afraid to fight, which was clearly
what remaining there would mean, but Brown would hear
about a brawl and find a way to use it against him. And
Ma would never forgive him if a free-for-all developed and
Sam sent his younger brother back to Keokuk with a cracked
skull or a pair of broken legs. So Sam swallowed his pride
and slipped out of the place with Henry. Behind them the
drunken mate hooted contemptuously.

Henry seemed on edge, even remote and standoffish when
they reached the street, but when he blurted out what was
on his mind Sam realized that his prudence in avoiding the
fight had nothing to do with the other's mood. "Sam, I'll go
crazy if I stay in Keokuk any longer."

"Doesn't Orion treat you well?"

"Sure, Sam—Orion's a fine man, especially when you know him as we do. But he can't afford to carry me, and I ought to be standing on my own feet."

How well Sam understood the restlessness that was nibbling at Henry—the beginning, as Macfarlane would say, of the great unlearning. "I'll take you around to the *Evening Post*. Sooner or later there'll be an opening in the composing room there."

Henry said, "Sam, I've been thinking. The best time I ever had in my life was with you, back on the *Journal* in Hannibal, when we put out those two issues while Orion was away."

A smile crossed Sam's face. "We woke 'em up!"

"But not Orion—not until it was too late. Then he admitted that if he had given you a freer hand maybe the *Journal* would have succeeded. That's why you have to love Orion. He can look square in a mirror and see all his faults."

"Orion's never had a real chance," Sam muttered, thinking that one day he'd give Orion just that.

"Sam," Henry said, getting to the truth at last, "I was hoping you could find me a spot on the *Pennsylvania*."

Oh, fine—so you can see what I take from Brown twelve hours out of every day, Sam thought. But Henry's eyes were pleading and said what he coudn't quite utter himself: "Dash-dang it, Sam, I want to be with you, like in those good old days back on the *Journal* in Hannibal!"

"I'll speak to the captain," Sam said briefly.

Klinefelter was a kindly man by nature, the *Pennsylvania* was a big boat, and help came and went. He gave Henry a trial and promised that, if he showed ability, he'd put him down next trip as third clerk in line of promotion. For Sam, Henry's presence aboard the *Pennsylvania* proved a godsend. No matter how brutally Brown's tongue lashed at him during a watch, Sam could depend on Henry to laugh and say, "Rats! It's over!"

Sam confessed to Henry that he had been scribbling again —random notes about the river and rivermen. He wondered now if he had been too hasty in burying Thomas Jefferson Snodgrass; maybe old Tom could have a relative with a more classical name, like Quintus Curtius Snodgrass.

"I should think that you could find a New Orleans paper interested in running river stuff," Henry said.

Sam nodded and, as Henry went off, summoned to an errand by Klinefelter, he leaned on the deck rail. Next time he tried to write, if he ever did, he'd get the right blend— the sharp, boyish buffoonery and fresh perception of Thomas Jefferson Snodgrass mixed with a dash of the worldly cynicism of the Scotsman Macfarlane. Off the bow the leadsman sang the sounding in a piercing chant. "Mark twain! mark twain! mark twain! mark twain! mark twain!" Sam stirred restlessly. Some old codger named Isaiah Sellers, a former pilot who gave the impression that he and Noah had sailed the first craft up the Mississippi, wrote articles for the *Picayune*. They invariably began, "My opinion for the benefit of the citizens of New Orleans is . . ."—the dullest trash Sam had ever read. Sellers always signed his pieces "Mark Twain." Sam thought he'd like to do a burlesque on Sellers some day. He could sign himself Sergeant Fathom, and for the benefit of the citizens of New Orleans relate a hairraising trip in 1763 on the old first *Jubilee*, piloting for a Chinese captain and a Choctaw crew.

Meanwhile, Sam needed spending money to jingle in his pockets, and New Orleans had to supply the answer. Watching freight on the levee during the night gave him five or six dollars for the two days the *Pennsylvania* stayed in port there. They were desolate nights for Sam, yet the money justified them. A tomb could not have been more mournfully deserted than was the levee. Not a creature moved; no dog barked, no cat mewed. Watching, waiting under the blinking stars, all sorts of memories flittered across Sam's mind. One concerned Henry—a dream that was still vivid, still deeply disturbing.

The incident had occurred on Sam's last visit to St. Louis. He had dreamed of Pamela's parlor, seeing clearly every detail of the room, even the music on the rack of the old piano. Across two chairs had rested a mahogany casket. Sam had walked across the room, peered into the casket, and recognized Henry's corpse. The reality of the dream had been so overpowering that when he awakened about four o'clock in the morning, he had dressed in a daze and gone out of the house. Grief-stricken, he wandered aimlessly through the streets of St. Louis. At last he returned to the house and forced himself to look into the parlor. There was no coffin, and Henry, coming down the stairs, called him to breakfast.

During the lonely vigils in New Orleans, Sam thought also of writing, turning over in his mind the lore of the river he had heard. Sometimes, he crammed plain hard facts into his memory. In March, 1825, General Lafayette had left New Orleans for St. Louis on the low-pressure steamer *Natchez*. In 1831 the Red River cutoff had formed. Other times, Sam recalled legends of the river and came to know fifty Lover's Leaps along the Mississippi from which Indian Maidens had jumped to their deaths.

Aboard the *Pennsylvania*, Sam's relations with Brown were no worse, only because that circumstance appeared to have become an impossibility. Sam picked his moments to sass back, in his own way.

"What are you steering for now?" Brown roared, seeing no mark.

Straight-faced, Sam gave the preposterous answer. "White

heifer over there on the bank." Brown foamed, and Sam let him.

Still, steam that was ever building up in a boiler eventually exploded it. Sam hoped that he could serve his time aboard the *Pennsylvania* without that happening. She was a grand boat and had taught him a great deal. But his hopes were in vain. At Eagle Bend, on the next trip down from St. Louis, Henry appeared in the pilot house. "Orders from Captain Klinefelter," he said. "Please stop at the next plantation landing."

At the wheel, Brown, who liked to pretend that he was deaf when the trick suited him, gave no sign that he had heard. Henry waited, embarrassed, but not a muscle twitched in the pilot's grim, belligerent face. Sam's eye caught Henry's, and he nodded for the boy to leave. Let Brown sulk if he pleased, Henry had carried out his duty.

The *Pennsylvania* steamed on, approached the plantation, but made no turn to land. Well, thought Sam, here's something new. The captain believes that he's running the boat, but we'll stop only if Mr. Brown cares to. They passed the landing.

Klinefelter appeared on the hurricane deck—a quiet, polite man. "Did Henry tell you to land here?" he asked Brown. "No, sir."

The captain turned to Sam, who had been handed the wheel at Klinefelter's entry. "Didn't you hear him?"

"Yes, sir."

"Shut your mouth!" Brown shouted at the cub. "You never heard anything of the kind!" Klinefelter bit his lip, but walked away.

Unaware of the discussion, Henry re-entered the wheelhouse almost immediately. Brown blazed at him. "Why didn't you tell me we had got to land at that plantation?"

"I did tell you, Mr. Brown."

"That's a lie!"

At the wheel, Sam said softly, "You lie yourself, Mr. Brown. Henry did tell you."

Brown looked as though Sam had slapped him. Then with a rush the blood came back into his face. "Get out'n the pilot house!" he bellowed at Henry.

The boy started to move when the pilot jumped at him. One hand caught Henry's collar and jerked him around. Brown's fist smashed Henry's face.

Sam let go of the wheel. In that blazing instant, for all he cared, the *Pennsylvania* could drift straight into kingdom come. Head down, he caught Brown in a leap. The two struggled, wavered, then Brown staggered. Sam pressed the pilot's long, bony body between his knees. Brown was trapped as ingloriously as a pig under a fence and he soon squealed more violently. Sam's left fist struck him, then the right, then the left, then the right. The pilot's head bounced like a ball on a string. Weeks, months of abuse, Mr. Brown —have one on the nose for that. Strike my little brother, will you, Mr. Brown—you can hold about two pounds of raw beef against that left eye.

The *Pennsylvania* drifted toward a treacherous sand bar. Sam clung to the howling, squirming Brown. By Godfrey, this was Old Testament retribution—this was sweet and wonderful revenge!

With a desperate heave, Brown finally shook off his infuriated cub. He sprang to the wheel and, for a weapon, snatched a spyglass. "Get out of this here pilot house!" he screamed.

"You should leave out the 'here,' " Sam said insolently. "It is understood and not considered good English form."

"Don't give me none of your airs! I ain't going to stand nothing more from you!"

"Say, 'Don't give me *any* of your airs.' " Sam corrected

the boiled lobster at the wheel. "The last half of your remark defies correction." Then he walked out.

Passengers, white-aproned servants, members of the crew waited on the forward deck. They greeted Sam with a lusty. cheer. He had given them a ripping good fight!

Sam swallowed hard. He must report now to Captain Klinefelter, confessing that he had broken the most sacred law of the river by striking the pilot on duty and deserting the wheel. There probably were more fingers on his hands than there were minutes remaining to his career as a riverman.

Henry waited in misery. He had ruined Sam's life, making Sam find him a job on the *Pennsylvania* and then precipitating this fight. He had always been a senseless burden to his brother, Henry thought, shuddering at the memory of himself as a sniveling kid who had hung on Ma's apron strings and outraged Sam with his nasty, self-righteous whining. In time his dull head had recognized the true Sam—a high-spirited, gay-hearted, wonderful brother who could twist the devil by the tail. Little by little he had won Sam's respect, acceptance, affection. And now? Henry groaned.

The door to Klinefelter's cabin opened. "Sam, did he sack you?" Henry asked, near tears at the thought. "How did it go? What did he say?"

"He asked me if I had struck Brown first. I said yes. Had I knocked him down? I said yes. Had I jumped on him? I said I had done worse—I had pinned him between my knees. Had I pounded him hard? I nodded. Had I pounded him— well, severely? The color was rising in Klinefelter's face. I said yes, I had pounded him pretty severely."

"Oh, Lord—what then, Sam?"

"Klinefelter cried, 'I'm deuced glad of it, Clemens!' He warned me not to do it again aboard *his* boat. As river crimes went, I couldn't be guiltier of a worse one. But the color stayed in his face. His voice dropped a note. 'Clemens,' he said, 'lay for him ashore! Give him a good sound thrashing, do you hear? I'll pay the expenses!' "

Henry broke into a grin. "That's a capital idea!"

"I declined the offer. Next time I might not stop until I had killed the devil, and Brown isn't worth a hanging."

When the watch ended, Brown stormed into Klinefelter's cabin. Either Sam left the boat at New Orleans, or Brown quit. The captain summoned Sam. Finding another pilot in New Orleans in early June was an impossibility. He would weep no tears if Brown left, the captain admitted. In fact, he would be very much relieved. Did Sam feel he could handle the wheel on the day watches if Ealer took all the night watches?

Sam shook his head. There were chutes around some of the islands he still didn't understand. "Sir, I think you better keep Brown till you reach St. Louis. Transfer me to another boat and let me follow you up river."

"That's your best judgment, Sam?"

"Yes, sir, it is."

"All right," Klinefelter said. "You knew the Bowens in Hannibal, and Bart Bowen pilots the *A. T. Lacey*. I'll see what I can do. Bart knows this river like the palm on his hand. He can teach you what you don't know about those chutes."

Henry slapped Sam on the back. "Things are going fine for the Clemens family. Orion's wife Mollie wrote that she's finally nudged the old buzzard into doing what he's always wanted to. He's selling the shop and moving to East Tennessee to study law!"

But Sam was edgy. He wondered what would happen now to Ma, and he was ill at ease at leaving Henry alone on the *Pennsylvania* with Brown.

"Great catfish, Sam," Henry exploded, "don't you think I'm ever going to grow up?"

Sam said seriously, "In case of trouble, keep your head, for the passengers will lose theirs. Rush to a boat on the hurricane deck and obey the mate. Help the women and children in, but don't get into a boat yourself. The river's seldom more than a mile wide. You can swim it easily."

"Oh, great catfish!" Henry moaned again.

Bart Bowen was delighted to have an old Hannibal resident aboard the *Lacey*. Bart was almost as square-faced as Will and every bit as homely, but he was good-hearted, full of fun, and a crack riverman. The *Lacey* followed the *Pennsylvania* by two days on the run to St. Louis, and Sam shared every watch in the pilot house with Bart.

Approaching Greenville, Mississippi, Bart was chuckling at one of Sam's stories when both noticed a man standing on the dock excitedly waving his arms. "Something's wrong, Sam. Go out and see what that fellow wants," Bart ordered.

Through cupped hands, the man on the dock bellowed at Sam, "The *Pennsylvania* blew up just below Memphis at Ship Island!"

Sam fought off a wave of nausea. His heart pounding, he shouted back, "Any casualties?"

"One hundred and fifty lives lost, sir. That's the report. It could be worse!"

19.

A Boy and a River

AT NAPOLEON, ARKANSAS, an extra edition of a Memphis
paper related some of the details of the accident. Bart's
finger jabbed eagerly at the list of those who had escaped
injury. "There's Henry's name!"

Sam read the line of type four times, staring at it with
a numb prayerfulness, fearing almost to lift his eyes for
fear Henry's name would disappear. "It could be a mistake,"
he muttered wretchedly. "Sometimes, rushing through an
extra, names are switched."

"Don't be a fool and borrow trouble," Bart grumbled.

Sam nodded, but he stole another glance at Henry's name.
"I put him on the river, Bart. I'll never forgive myself if
anything happens to him."

Details of the accident in the Memphis extra were sparse.
At six o'clock on a warm mid-June morning the *Pennsylvania* had tied to a barge carrying wood. She was loading
fuel for the day's run. At that time Ealer was probably in
the wheelhouse, Sam reminded himself. He'd be running
under full steam to carry the extra load. Most of the passengers
had been asleep when the *Pennsylvania* exploded. Four of
her eight boilers had blown.

Sam paced the hurricane deck of the *Lacey*, savage in his

anxiety to reach another Arkansas port—Australia or Helena
—where he could secure a later paper. Australia was seven
or eight hours up river, Helena another five. One place or
another should have fuller reports.

Bart came off duty. "You going to turn in, Sam?"

"I can't sleep till I see another paper."

"I'll have to—you know what these night watches are.
Call me if you learn anything more."

Sam nodded dully, clutching the Memphis extra as though
it was his only hope. His mind filled in what must have
happened aboard the *Pennsylvania* when the boilers gave
way. An explosion like that would have blown out the whole
front of the boat. The real killer to dread then was scalding
steam getting into your lungs. Likely the chimneys had been
ripped apart. Dry weather, hot embers—the *Pennsylvania*
would turn into a ghastly inferno.

Grimly, Sam stared at the river, remembering that some
called the Mississippi by another name. River of Grief and
Tears! Every drop of water that washed by the *Lacey* had
traveled fifteen hundred miles to reach that point. Sam's old
boyhood fears of the unknown and the supernatural disturbed him as though he were still eight years of age. Other
drops of water had fulfilled the work the devil had set
them to; they had flowed those fifteen hundred miles to
form the steam that had blown up the *Pennsylvania!*

Henry! Sam spoke the name prayerfully to the stars.
Dear God, let there be no mistake in the Memphis extra!
Henry must live, and Sam must meet again that same fine,
fair-skinned, kindhearted boy with whom he had parted in
New Orleans! Around Sam rose the sounds of boat and
river—the water washing off the paddle wheels, the bells
clanging on the bouncing buoys in the channel. His glance
caught the silver glints of moonlight dancing over the
rippled surface of the Mississippi. River of Grief and Tears!

Easily, Sam realized, love could turn to hatred—the kind of love that betrayed, that broke a life, that twisted destiny into a mean and crippled thing.

At Helena the late paper had arrived. Sam read down the column and sank to the bench in the pilot house, holding his head between his hands and letting the hot, dry sobs shake him. On the list of those scalded beyond hope of recovery was the name of Henry Clemens. Oh, God, Sam had really known since that dream in St. Louis when he had peered into the mahogany casket.

"You can't tell," Bart said stubbornly. "They've brought the best doctors they can find into Memphis. They'll pull some through!"

"They'll die like flies," Sam moaned. He knew, he knew. Oh, River of Grief and Tears—betrayer, killer!

From landing to landing, the story of the tragedy aboard the *Pennsylvania* assumed more frightening dimensions. Not one hundred and fifty lives had been lost, but more nearly three hundred! Klinefelter had been in the barbershop when the boilers burst. Beside his chair, when the flying timbers and steam had cleared, had stood the barber—still mixing his lather in a senseless stupor, his foot half extending over a gaping hole. Both the captain and the barber had walked out alive. Some, like Brown, had been asleep and had simply vanished as though a hand had reached out of heaven, seized and crumpled their bodies, and scattered the dust on the waves of the Mississippi. In the pilot house Ealer, at the wheel, had heard the blast and seen the chimneys toppling. He had flung his coat over his head, protecting nose and mouth and eyes from the scalding steam, and thus had escaped.

A public hall in Memphis served as an emergency hospital. Sam pushed through the crowd at the door, searched frantically among the rows of mattresses on the floor, and at last found Henry—alive, but so limp, so hurt, so helpless and hopeless. He had inhaled steam, and his body was frightfully scalded.

Day after day Sam sat by his brother. On a piece of paper dated Friday, June 18, 1858, he wrote Orion's wife Mollie, "The horrors of three days have swept over me—they have blasted my youth and left me an old man before my time." Those who watched Sam, remaining hour after hour by Henry's side, knew how truthfully he wrote. Before their eyes Sam's hair was turning prematurely gray. In his desperate helplessness and hopelessness he cried to Mollie, "Long before this reaches you my poor Henry—my darling, my pride, my glory, my *all* will have gone out in utter darkness." He ended pitifully. "Pray for me, Mollie, and pray for my poor sinless brother."

Bit by bit Sam pieced together from the accounts of other survivors how Henry had lived through the fateful end of the *Pennsylvania*. The explosion had blown him into the river. The shore was only a few hundred feet away, and he had begun swimming toward it. He had felt no pain and believed himself unhurt, so he had turned back to assist in the rescue of others. No one knew who had pulled him out of the river when he collapsed. He had been lifted onto a wood flat and left there until medical help could arrive. For hours a burning sun had beaten down on him.

Sam groaned. How wise Macfarlane had been! How cruel and wicked a thing was life that betrayed Henry when he wanted only to save others, that trapped Jim under the roots of a tree in the Illinois bottoms, that burned alive poor Dennis McDermid for wanting to smoke his pipe before retiring to a cheerless bed, that killed off Pa when for the first time in years his future had begun to look bright. Oh, Universe of Grief and Tears!

The sufferings of the first mate tortured Sam through

those bitter days. Three times they carted the delirious, raving man to the dead room, and three times they carted him back. His burns were horrible, but he refused to take morphine. Terror-stricken of this newly discovered drug, he accused doctors and nurses of trying to murder him by mixing it in his water and his other medicine. Although his parched throat and lips screamed for water after each bout of delirium, he would not touch it. Among the groaning, suffering victims of the room would rise a sudden roar—the first mate, in his delirium, believing he was still on the *Pennsylvania* and screaming at the crew. "Hump yourselves, you petrifactions, snail-bellies, pallbearers! Going to be all day getting that hatful of freight out?" The outburst ceased presently. He fell back on his mattress. No one would trick him into taking morphine. He had the will; he'd live. He did.

On the sixth day, Dr. Peyton, who had watched over Henry almost as lovingly as though he were his own son, gave Sam his first hope. Henry had rallied that day; perhaps the danger was past. "I believe he will get well," the old Memphis practitioner said. "He is likely to be restless during the night; the groans and fretting of the others may disturb him. If he cannot rest, tell the physician in charge to give him one-eighth of a grain of morphine."

Sam nodded happily. He watched Henry slumbering, and after a time napped also. But Henry's groaning and tossing suddenly bolted Sam back into wakefulness. Cold with panic, he fled to find the physician in charge.

A young medical student appeared to be the only person in attendance. Sam explained Dr. Peyton's instructions about the morphine. The student looked uncomfortable. "Sir," he told Sam, "I know nothing about these new drugs. Likely you're unduly alarmed. Go back and sit by your brother a while longer."

Sam bit his lip, retracing his way along the row of mattresses. Henry seemed even more restless. His hands clutched at the sheet. Sam went back to find the student. He felt terrorized. "Give him the one-eighth grain of morphine," Sam begged. "Surely you've been taught to measure out that much of anything!"

The student hesitated, then with a wan smile he said, "Well, there's always the old-fashioned way. That would be about as much as you can hold on the point of a knife blade."

The drug put Henry into a heavy sleep. He never awakened.

The family came back to St. Louis from Hannibal, where Henry was buried. Orion, smoking one of Sam's cigars, sat in Pamela's front parlor and inquired when his brother planned to go back to steamboating.

Sam started to say, "Never!" He hated the river! How could he go back, seeing Henry's face in every glint of sunlight upon the water? Then he looked at poor Orion's threadbare suit and realized that the only cigars his brother ever enjoyed were those others gave him. Now that Orion was studying law, heaven only knew how he'd get along without some help. If his experience was like Pa's, financial success for Orion might be ten thousand years away! And Sam thought of Ma and her Kentucky pride; she couldn't sponge on Orion and wouldn't want to sponge on Pamela and her husband. Ma would wither away to bones and no skin if she relied on the Tennessee land for her livelihood.

"I'll be going back to the river as soon as I can get another boat," Sam said, answering Orion. "Horace Bixby should be back in St. Louis any day, and my affairs will straighten out then."

"Keep going—only way you can stand to live," Orion

said with a nod, and Sam wondered if Orion's lectures always
had made that much sense.

In September Sam received his license as a pilot, and
Bixby took him into the pilot house as his partner. But Sam,
as Bixby said, possessed more brains than most rivermen. It
pleased the old tutor when his former cub was advanced
almost overnight to pilot of the *City of Memphis*, the new
queen of the Mississippi fleet. Sam could now help his mother
and brother handsomely, and a note of honest pride filled
his letter to Orion.

> Putting all things together, I begin to think I am rather
> lucky than otherwise—a notion which I was slow to take
> up. The other night I was about to "round to" for a storm,
> but concluded that I could find a smoother bank somewhere.
> I landed five miles below. The storm came, passed away and
> did not injure us. Coming up, day before yesterday, I
> looked at the spot I first chose, and half the trees on the
> bank were torn to shreds. We couldn't have lived five min-
> utes in such a tornado. And I am also lucky in having a
> berth, while all the other young pilots are idle. This is the
> luckiest circumstance that ever befell me. Not on account
> of the wages—for that is a secondary consideration—but from
> the fact that the *City of Memphis* is the largest boat in the
> trade, and the hardest to pilot, and consequently I can get a
> *reputation* on her, which is a thing I never could accomplish
> on a transient boat. I can "bank" in the neighborhood of $100
> a month on her, and that will satisfy me for the present
> (principally because the other youngsters are *sucking their
> fingers*). Bless me! What a pleasure there is in revenge—and
> what vast respect Prosperity commands! Why, six months
> ago, I could enter the "Rooms," and receive only the custom-
> ary fraternal greeting—now they say, "Why, how *are* you,
> old fellow—when did you get in?"

And the young pilots who used to tell me, patronizingly,

that I could never learn the river cannot keep from showing a little of their chagrin at seeing me so far ahead of them. Permit me to "blow my horn," for I derive a *living* pleasure from these things, and I must confess that when I go to pay my dues, I rather like to let the dash-dang rascals get a glimpse of a hundred-dollar bill peeping out from amongst notes of smaller dimensions whose face I do *not* exhibit! You will despise this egotism, but I tell you there is a "stern joy" in it.

A strange thing began happening to Sam. Most dreams that had dominated his life had come in one vivid flash, but this dream kept repeating itself—for days, for months, for years—and changing and growing and seeming more real than *actual* reality! Under this spell, Sam stood, holding the wheel of the great *City of Memphis*, with a twinkle in his eyes and a smile touching his mouth so gently that he looked more like the happy voyager who had sailed this old river in a "borrowed" skiff. He had always known that sooner or later the emergency would arise; and so Sam began his dream, not surprised at all.

When the door to the pilot house jerked open, there stood the mate, grinning maliciously, and holding by the ear the defiant, monstrously freckled-faced boy he had found hiding under the lifeboat. "What do I do with *this?*" the mate sneered, giving the ear a smart pinch.

"Is it human?" Sam said, trained to the finest points of piloting.

"Looks to be. It's alive, at any rate."

"Fish bite awfully good on stowaway boys—those two-hundred-pound catfish that run up river."

"Sir, you can't cut up better bait."

Sam glanced down at the sullen, cowering boy, whose sandy hair was slicked down so that even a proud mother

couldn't find the hint of a curl and whose face, like Will
Bowen's, was square and homely. The boy's bare feet were
dirty and calloused and he kept snapping his big toe to
bolster his courage. Sam knew what came next. He was
supposed to ask the boy's name and advise him to change
the silly thing, and then ask whence he came and hoot at
the stupidity of the collective residents of that absurd river
landing. Then he would tell the mate to give the lad "the
usual treatment" and chuckle as the mate dragged the victim
off to the Siberia of the ladies' lounge.

Well, Sam couldn't play the part. He couldn't forget
that quickly. To get rid of the mate, Sam said gruffly, "Go
down and have the leadsman take the sounding all over
again. I think he was drunk when he took it last time."

The mate obeyed, spinning his fingers around the side
of his head as soon as he was out of sight to show what he
thought of Sam.

"You go check on that drunken mate," Sam told his
flabbergasted cub, deciding that it was in the public interest
for the mentally deranged to have their insanity well publi-
cized. Now, he had the stowaway to himself, and he turned
to duty—as he conceived it.

"What's your name, son?"

"Huck—short for Huckleberry."

"I mean what were you christened?"

"I was doused—that is christened, sir, meanin' no irreverence—Tom."

"Tom what?"

"Tom Sawyer."

"Now that's a mighty fine name for a boy, son. So's
Huck. I can see where it'd be hard to choose between 'em."

"Mind, sir, if I limber my gums with a chaw of terbacker?"

"No, Huck, if you can stomach the stuff. I couldn't at
your age."

"I ain't got to seegars, yet."

"Well, if you ever do, let me give you some advice. Never smoke 'em more'n one at a time."

"I guess not."

"Say, Huck, you ever know a runaway slave?"

"I guess so."

"You turn him in?"

"No, sir! I leave mean-hearted actions for the grownups. I've got more valuable things to do with my time."

"Like exploring caves?"

"That's the sport."

"And roasting stolen potatoes?"

"Spuds would jes' be left over an' rot away, anyhow."

"And gathering pecans over in the Illinois bottoms?"

"They're the best."

"In a borrowed skiff?"

"How'd I get there otherwise?"

"Huck, what do you know about Satan?"

"Just about everything."

"I thought so," Sam said as the mate and the cub, sticking close together for mutual protection, re-entered the pilot house.

"The sounding," the mate said, "was correctly reported. Mark twain."

"Thank you," Sam said politely. "Now you and the cub go back and thank the leadsman and tell him to jump into the river, and then you and the cub jump in after him."

"Y-y-yes, sir!" the mate said, dragging the cub with him to the safety of the hurricane deck.

"Say," the boy said, "there's nothing more wonderful'n bein' a river pilot, is there?"

"Not at your age."

"Say, was that your name? What he said—Mark Twain?"

"Well, I was doused—that is christened, Huck, meanin' no irreverence—Sam Clemens."

"I like Mark Twain better. Has a nice trim river sound."

"It does at that."

"I sure hope I meet you again, Mr. Mark Twain."

"I hope so too, Huck or Tom Sawyer—whichever I think to call you."

"Well, take your pick. I got a few special friends I can take almost anything from!"

Nobody has to believe that anything even remotely resembling this dream occurred—even in Sam's fancy. Anyone who was too practical for any such dash-dang nonsense only made Sam remember what Macfarlane had said about the low place of man in the animal kingdom.

Anyhow, no boy ever doubts it.

Postscript

Sam's dream was never forgotten through the long years he roamed the world as miner, journalist, lecturer, and author. Always the old river and his boyhood days in Hannibal were a love that lived in his heart, and ultimately he gave both immortality through the pages of *The Adventures of Tom Sawyer*, *The Adventures of Huckleberry Finn*, and *Life on the Mississippi*.

Although many sources were used in re-creating Sam's world and life from his Hannibal days to his emergence as a pilot on the Mississippi, the author wishes to acknowledge his special indebtedness to three books: *Mark Twain: The Personal and Literary Life of Samuel Langhorne Clemens* in three volumes by Albert Bigelow Paine (New York, 1912); *Samuel Clemens of Hannibal* by Dixon Wecter (Boston, 1952); and *Mark Twain, Son of Missouri* by Minnie M. Brashear (Chapel Hill, 1934).

Unless otherwise noted, the characters in this book are drawn from persons Sam actually knew. Below is a discussion, chapter by chapter, of where fact and fancy divide.

1. *Sam Clemens, Sinner*. Sam's overactive conscience, and his attraction to Satan are well known. No frontier town of the period can be truly depicted without its drunkards, its temperance crusaders, and its religious revivalists. Tom Blankenship, the original of Huck Finn, failed to fulfill the dismal future predicted for him and rose in later years to

the respectable position of justice of the peace in a Western town. Whereas Tom Sawyer is largely a self-portrait of Sam as a boy in Hannibal, a considerable amount of Will Bowen also went into Tom. In real life, Injun Joe was not the sinister person known to Huck Finn or Tom Sawyer. The toe-snapping ability actually belonged to Arch Fuqua, a character who does not appear in these pages, and so his remarkable talent has been loaned to Gull Brady.

2. *Sam and Henry*. Pamela's implication in the plot concerning the cats and the game of Catfish are the author's inventions. Henry Clemens during these tender years provided Sam with the model for the intolerable Sid Sawyer in *The Adventures of Tom Sawyer*.

3. *Mostly About Cats*. The affair in the Western Star Tavern happened.

4. *Stowaway*. Sam certainly *did* punch Henry. Five or six times during his boyhood Sam almost succeeded in drowning, and if Ma appears to be somewhat blasé in this instance, perhaps she should be forgiven. The Clemenses' continual economic struggle to survive and their hope that someday the Tennessee land would make them rich were dominant themes in Sam's early years. Sam's adventures as a stowaway generally followed the pattern of this chapter. The pilot of the *Jeanie Deans*, and the deck hands, Ed and Mike, are imaginary.

5. *On the Farm*. The incidents of this chapter are all based on fact, but although the dogs did wrangle with the hogs under the church floor, no one can be sure that Sam was ever responsible for setting them to it. (I'll wager he did.)

6. *Cross Mr. Cross*. The incidents of Sam's emergence as a poet, with the dire consequences that followed, and Will's acquisition of the "trained louse," again with dire consequences, are true. Poor old Cross has been somewhat exag-

gerated as a type of cane-switching schoolmaster along the frontier.

7. *Cave Hollow*. The existence of the guns and the cadaver in the copper cylinder were known to Sam; his discovery of them as here depicted is imaginary.

8. *Sam Can't Wait*. A Hannibal newspaper of the time declared that only one out of four babies born reached the age of one year, and only one out of two lived to be twenty-one. Sam still thought the possible reward justified the terrible risk of getting into bed with Will Bowen during the measles epidemic. And he did fake the attack of worms.

9. *Bence*. 10. *Jim*. These two chapters are an allegory, representing Sam's struggle as a boy born in slaveholding country to reconcile the "institution" to a sensitive character that cried to be free. The known facts are that Bence fed the runaway slave, and that Sam was with the party when the Negro was found in the morass. In *Huckleberry Finn*, Sam wrote his greatest tribute to human nobility in the scenes in which a shiftless river rat protects Jim at any cost. Bence's problem, however, was not that he conspired against the law to protect the slave—that would have been Sam's problem—but a choice between the reward and human freedom, which he valued more. In later life Sam's firm opposition to human bondage extended even to King Leopold's brutalities in the Congo. So the allegory is justified; the character of Sam as it grew is the essential *fact* to portray. Doubtless Bence was the model for Tom Sawyer and Huck Finn's great friend, Muff Potter. Dates have been altered throughout this sequence to simplify the telling of a story.

Jane Clemens' attitudes toward slavery, as cited in Chapters 4 and 10, are based on reliable sources. Sam actually witnessed the murder of the slave with the piece of iron ore.

11. *Printer's Devil.* Sam's missing a word in the spelling bee, the rolling of the rocks down Holliday's (or Cardiff) Hill, and the circumstances of Pa's death, are true. Sam's troubled conscience, his promise to Ma, his apprenticeship under Ament are also factual. Nor did Sam ever lose his hero worship of Joan of Arc. In time, he dreamed of making *The Personal Recollections of Joan of Arc* his crowning work, but a Mississippi boyhood was to provide that triumph and a runaway slave named Jim to become his purest character!

12. *Sam and Orion.* Ma and Pamela maneuvered Orion into his hapless career as a publisher, and Sam's association with Orion covers a period of about six years. Sam bedeviled poor Jim Wolfe at least as badly as in the three incidents here taken from the record, and Jim's conduct in the fire did launch Sam into his first writing.

13. *Cub Editor.* The issue in which Sam did his boyish best to resuscitate the *Journal* was published on September 16, 1852.

14. *A Widening Rift.* The unhappy ending of Dennis McDermid and its tremendous impact upon Sam are factual, as is Sam's break with Orion over the gun and his pledge to Ma before leaving Hannibal.

15. *The Wanderer.* Sam's letters home during his stay in New York and Philadelphia supply the material for almost all of this chapter. The foreman at Gray's is imaginary. Frog combines the irritabilities of two old compositors who worked for the *Inquirer*.

16. *Thomas Jefferson Snodgrass.* Sam's conversation about writing is cited as occurring with a boarder whom he victimized into lighting his water pipe, but it takes no great imagination to see and hear Henry in the same role. The pranks on the music teacher happened. The tale Sam tells

about the bugs is adapted from a letter to Annie Taylor. The proposed trip to the Amazon, and the finding of the fifty-dollar note are true; the conversation with the managing editor of the *Keokuk Post* is imaginary, but not the agreement reached. Two Snodgrass letters were published. Macfarlane did have his own theory of evolution antedating the publication of Darwin's *Descent of Man*. The New Orleans experiences, related here and later, are from a letter Sam wrote Ma.

17. *Bixby's Cub.* In *Life on the Mississippi* Sam exaggerated the rather mild-mannered Bixby, combining the characteristics of several pilots he knew. Sam's explanation of a pilot's knowledge and how his memory works is drawn from Chapter 13 of that book.

18. *River Feud.* 19. *A Boy and a River.* Sam gives his own version of his bitter experiences with Brown, the fight, and the death of Henry in *Life on the Mississippi*. Other facts have been added. A few letters under the pseudonym of Quintus Curtius Snodgrass were published in 1861 in a New Orleans newspaper, and, of course, in time Sam did appropriate Isaiah Seller's pen name, Mark Twain. The letter to Orion after Sam became pilot of the *City of Memphis* is authentic.

It was always Sam's belief that no fact should get in the way of a good story, and to write a story about Sam Clemens (and it is terribly difficult not to call him Tom Sawyer) and such friends as Tom Blankenship (who seems to keep peering over an author's shoulder and whispering, "I reckon I won't give it too much mind if you do slip an' call me Huck Finn") sets its own standard: you tell the story as it comes to you. When Sam published *The Adventures of Huckleberry Finn*, he attached his own terse warning:

NOTICE

PERSONS attempting to find a motive in this narrative will be prosecuted; persons attempting to find a moral in it will be banished; persons attempting to find a plot in it will be shot.

BY ORDER OF THE AUTHOR,
Per G. G., Chief of Ordnance.

And no one has yet invented a better way of letting a story write itself.

E.S.M.

ABOUT THE AUTHOR

EARL SCHENCK MIERS long has made American history his major interest. Well known are such books as *The Rainbow Book of American History* (for young people), *Gettysburg, The General Who Marched to Hell,* and *The Web of Victory;* also, in collaboration with Paul M. Angle, he has edited a one-volume edition of the writings of Abraham Lincoln. Born May 27, 1910, in Brooklyn, New York, he was graduated from Rutgers University, and also is the recipient of an honorary degree. He is a member of Phi Beta Kappa. He is the father of two sons, David and William, and a daughter, Meredith.

THIS BOOK WAS SET IN
JANSON AND NICOLAS COCHIN TYPES BY
SLUGS COMPOSITION COMPANY.
IT WAS PRINTED AND BOUND BY
THE HADDON CRAFTSMEN.
THE PAPER IS PERKINS AND SQUIER COMPANY'S
RRR SMOOTH ANTIQUE
MADE BY P. H. GLATFELTER COMPANY.
TYPOGRAPHY AND DESIGN ARE BY
LAWRENCE S. KAMP